ARTIFACTS OF
THE SIMULATION:
A Reference Book
for Simulation Theory

~~~~~~~~~~~~~~~~~~

Written by

Jason M. Pittman

&

Frank Scalambrino

Winston-Salem, NC: Pirino Books
MMXXII

Winston-Salem, NC: Pirino Books.
Pittman, Jason M.
Scalambrino, Frank
Includes bibliographic references and index.
ISBN: 979-8218012380 (Paperback)
1. Simulation Theory 2. Simulation Argument
3. Simulation Hypothesis 4. Cyborg Anthropology.

14 13 12 11 10 9 8 7 6

Pirino: aurora ignis aquarii

List of Figures and Films:

Figures:

Films:

Lo and Behold, Reveries of the Connected World (2016, NetScout Documentary),

Westworld (2016, HBO TV Series),

The Simulation Hypothesis (2015, Fair Wind Documentary),

Limitless (2011, Relativity Media),

Inception (2010, Warner Bros.),

The Butterfly Effect (2004, New Line Cinema),

Robo Sapiens (2004, Discovery Channel Documentary),

12 Monkeys (1996, Universal Pictures).

Table of Contents

Dedication

Dr. Jason M. Pittman:

For my family and friends, your unconditional support has my eternal gratitude.

For everyone unafraid to pursue Truth, may this work provide you with a worthy roadmap.

For the random people I interrogated about the nature of reality, the possibility of Simulation, and other strange ideas, thank you for your patience and honesty.

Dr. Frank Scalambrino:

I see this work as a contribution to future generations and conversations. I sincerely believe this book functions as a context, overview, and reference for all future thinking regarding Simulation Theory; and, I believe anyone interested in Simulation Theory will find this book helpful. It is to that which I dedicate this work.

Acknowledgements

Dr. Pittman:

Foremost, I would like to acknowledge my long-time friend and coauthor, Dr. Frank Scalambrino. Our frequent, long conversations have been the highlight of the past few years. Authoring a book isn't easy. Authoring a book with a coauthor is not necessarily easier. Despite the added complexities, having you as a colleague made this easy and fun. I couldn't imagine having a better experience. I genuinely believe we have achieved something special here, and it wouldn't have been possible without your help.

I also want to acknowledge the legion of thinkers, researchers, academics, and question-askers who enrich the body of human knowledge. Not all ideas are good, but the idea not explored remains forever bad.

Lastly, I want to acknowledge the potential absurdity on one hand and potential truth on the other of Simulation Theory. The idea we reside in an illusion of sorts isn't new. It may be utter bullshit. However, if we don't explore the idea, we will never know one way or the other. So, go forth dear explorers and find the boundaries of our reality.

Dr. Scalambrino:

I would like to acknowledge Dr. Jason M. Pittman my long-time friend and coauthor. I very much enjoyed the process of writing this book with him. I look forward to our future collaborations.

I received no outside funding or sabbatical with which to write this book.

Thank you for purchasing this book.

Preface

Dr. Jason M. Pittman

Reality might be a Simulation. That thought is at once stupendously impressive and terrifying.

The idea of our reality, my reality, being a Simulation is impressive to me as a computational theorist. Further, as a habitual tinkerer, I tend to want to understand the inner workings of the *things*.

However, the idea of living in a Simulation is terrifying because I don't know if we could tell we are in fact in a Simulation and because I don't know who designed, implemented, and is maintaining the inner workings of it. Oddly enough, such terror drives me to want to understand the inner workings of the Simulation.

From my perspective, this work is a description of the *how, what,* and *when* related to Simulation Theory. I recall spending hours discussing those three words with Dr. Scalambrino before the three adverbs took their final form as questions. The more I assumed I was in a Simulation, the more curious I became about base reality. Specifically, I increasingly wondered about the machine in base reality responsible for generating the Simulation.

My contributions to this work are in the context of exposing the attributes or characteristics of the Simulation in a computational context. My ability to offer philosophical analysis of the Simulation argument is limited. I instantly saw how to contribute from a computational perspective though. That being said, I don't know that I noticed something peculiar about the structure of the questions until I sat down to craft my part of this Preface.

Can you spot the peculiarity in the structure? Read through them slowly...

What is being simulated?

How is what is being simulated, simulated?

When is how what is being simulated simulated, simulated?

I admit the questions are awkwardly worded. The nested repetition is intentional because it reflects how I structured my content across and within the chapters. Nested repetition, or *recursion*, also happens to be a critical element in computer science. The choice and position of adverbs and questions are deliberate as well. These serve as fantastic guide stones for the complex journey through Simulation Theory. Well, that is if we have done our job well.

My writing process consisted of two parts: asking a question, writing down the answer. You can try it for yourself. For the magic to work, you must ask the question aloud.

What is simulated at the Social level of resolution?

Our answer is in Chapter 1, section 2 and hopefully reads as a conversation between friends over a coffee or beer. With this in mind, If I had any advice whatsoever as to how to read this book, it is to (1) frame the chapter and section (and subsection) headings as questions; (2) write down your short answer; (3) read our answers; (4) and finally, compare answers and revise your thinking accordingly.

Maybe we are living in a Simulation. Maybe not. What is for certain, this work will help you figure it out for yourself.

Finally, I would like to point out again how this work is the culmination of several years of phone calls, in-person meetings, and tireless partnership with Dr. Scalambrino.

More importantly this book became a means to spend meaningful time with a longtime friend and colleague. For that, I am eternally grateful.

Jason M. Pittman, Sc.D.
February 2022
Winston-Salem, NC

Dr. Frank Scalambrino

On the one hand, in 2015 the two of us were involved with, and published material regarding, the concept of "technological mediation" with the Social Epistemology Review & Reply Collective (SERRC) and Roman & Littlefield International. The idea, of course, being that the technology mediating our *experience* of the environment changes us and our *experience* of the environment, along with the *environment*. The ideas of "cyborg anthropology" and existentialism provide context for these insights and illuminate a kind of equality-based soteriology in the face of the technological alteration of human existence.

On the other hand, our current project takes the popular question, "Do we live in a Simulation?" as its point of departure. We humbly and sincerely believe that we have worked out the logic of the possible ways that it could be true that we "live in a Simulation." In fact, we have developed a "matrix" to graphically represent the possible ways to affirmatively answer the question. The three major categories of the matrix are: the Actual, the Virtual, and the Mental. Each category, then, has the following three sub-categories: the Universal, the Social, and the Individual.

We believe this matrix covers all the possible ways to affirmatively answer the question, "Do we live in a Simulation?" The book, then, develops an articulation of each of the positions in the matrix. We sincerely believe this book will be indispensably valuable to anyone and everyone interested in the Simulation question, because it ultimately functions as "the gameboard," so to speak, for all the possible moves one could make in attempting to advance an affirmative response to the central question of Simulation Theory. No one else has provided such a gameboard for Simulation Theory. We truly believe that because, logically, there are no positions that a person could take outside of the positions we elucidate, our book should stand the test of time as a foundational text for Simulation Theory.

Frank Scalambrino, Ph.D.
May 16, 2022
Old Colorado City
Colorado, USA

Introduction

Are we living in a machine-generated Simulation?

If so, how would we know?

If you can tell that we live in a Simulation, what are the features or characteristics giving away the illusion?

These questions, and more, are the subjects explored in the documentary *A Glitch in the Matrix*. Released in February 2021, the film quickly garnered a word-of-mouth following. The title itself is a reference to another popular film, *The Matrix* in which one of the main characters explains that glitches occur in the simulated world inhabited by the characters when the machines controlling the Simulation make a change to it. Colloquially, to say one has experienced a glitch in the Matrix is to say there has been an unexplained (unexplainable?) phenomenological event.

Back to the documentary- the filmmaker purports to have collected, *philosophical evidence and scientific explanation* in support of an affirmative conclusion. That is, we live in a Simulation. Without a doubt, the documentary is not the first or only source to reach such a conclusion. Indeed, the film is more of a collection of conclusions organized within an overarching narrative. Importantly, the source material connects thematically with one another. There are gaps which is where this work comes in. Analysis of the source material is necessary to properly contextualize the material. The expected outcome is a delta consisting of measures of meaning or artifacts.

The analysis of evidence and construction of meaning is the straightforward goal of this work. More specifically, the goal is to go beyond the veil and lay down a series of artifacts. We intend the artifacts to be guide stones for thinking about Simulation Theory. These artifacts serve as anchors and waypoints as you wind along whatever path you synthesize. At the very least, we view this work as setting up an internal consistency and guiding logic for the themes of Simulation Theory.

§1 Source Material

§1.1 *The Matrix* Films & the *A Glitch in the Matrix* Documentary

Indeed, one of the more prominent themes coming out of *The Matrix* is the sense that too perfect of a Simulation led human minds to reject that Simulation. Thus, the machines resorted to introducing imperfections into the Simulations with the intent of making the reality more believable, more real. Indirectly, this connects to the questions (or at least the spirit of the questions) we opened the chapter with: could you tell you're in a Simulation and, if so, how?

Furthermore- and more germane to the relation between the film, the documentary, and the overall concept of the Simulation Hypothesis- the glitch term used in *A Glitch in the Matrix* stems directly from *The Matrix* both in use and form.

The hallmark scene discussed heavily in the documentary, is the déjà vu interaction as the antagonists are making to leave the Simulation. In *The Matrix*, the protagonists set up déjà vu as synonymous with a change in the simulated reality, what they refer to as a glitch. While not said explicitly, there is a deeper relation insofar as glitch and change become intertwined. Any glitch then signals a change to the state Simulation running on the base reality machine substrate.

By way of analogy, the idea is like a programmer making a code change to a website. The web browser will reloads the page once the change is deployed. Often the change and reload occur without the user noticing. Occasionally there is an artifact left on our screen that we do notice.

Meanwhile, the scientific explanation[1] of *déjà vu* explains why we experience the phenomenon. We should note the explanation does not rule out the underlying why mechanisms as the result of a base reality programming construct. We have the ability to rigorously describe the cognitive and neurological mechanisms leading to perceiving déjà vu. There is nothing in the science precluding a computational machine from simulating those mechanisms.

There are other connections between *The Matrix* and the Simulation Hypothesis. For example, take the idea of partial rendering and exclusiveness of simulated reality discussed in the context of Bostrom's paper. On one hand, all the humans in the Matrix are experiencing the same matrix. Yet, external inputs can target specific humans. The protagonists answering phones to unload, or escape, is one example. Another example is the agents loading into the Simulation and take over projected human avatars. Further, causes in the Simulation have effects outside of the Simulation (e.g., grievous wounds in the Matrix can be lethal).

As well, we should point out that the humans outside of the Matrix can create and load themselves into a diminutive version of the Matrix they call the construct. This is a nested Simulation which is entirely plausible given how advanced humanity's technology seemed to be in the movie and as described during expositional elements.

§1.2 The Philip K. Dick Lecture

The Matrix and its sequels express the collective themes from Philip K. Dick's (PKD)[2] fiction well. Unabashedly a master of science-fiction, PKD wrote extensively about speculative technologies and realities: *Do Androids Dream*

---

[1] Ling, T. (2021). What causes déjà vu? The quirky neuroscience behind the memory. Science Focus.
[2] Dick, P. K. (1995). The Shifting Realities of Philip K. Dick: Selected Literary and Philosophical Writings. Vintage.

of Electric Sheep, Ubik, and *A Scanner Darkly.* Throughout his body of work, Philip K. Dick emphatically maintained that we inhabit a programmed reality lateral to other realities. He claimed to discover the truth behind simulated reality during a medicinal hallucination some years prior. The exposure to this alternative but equally as real timeline inspired much of his science fiction writing, most notably *The Man in the High Castle* which recently was a hit Amazon Prime show between 2015 and 2019. Indeed, he sprinkled clues leading to his Simulation Hypothesis throughout his fiction. However, it was in his Metz Lecture, as it has come to be known, where PKD revealed two important thoughts about the Simulation Hypothesis.

First, PKD was explicit throughout the Metz Lecture about Simulations interlinking through what he referred to as "*orthogonal*" time. This means Simulations adjacent to our reality layer atop our linear timeline. Our simulated present aligns with adjacent present times. It helps to think of orthogonal time as an infinite ladder with the rungs being the right angles linking other Simulations to the experienced reality.

Less obvious is the implications of this clue to the computational apparatus running or powering the Simulations. For one thing, the orthogonal temporal linkage suggests *all* Simulations are running atop a common substrate. Alternatively, the Simulations could run on discrete substrates that are themselves linked orthogonally. I hesitate to write "*hardware*" because it might lead to imagining too specific of a machine. Later in this book, we will discuss more definitive substrate ideas.

In the meantime, it is important to mention how PKD's thesis indicates that the set of all Simulations draws upon a shared asset collection for the events, phenomena, and so forth rendered therein. This is, in contrast, to two Simulations with completely different assets, rendered elements, and critically with disjoint timelines.

Introduction

Second, the existence of simulated realities presupposes the existence of *base reality*. In fact, PKD directly refers to base reality numerous times during the Metz Lecture. The base reality is a reality in which at least two entities exist: the Programmer and the Machine. The Programmer builds and runs the Simulations while the Machine is some form of technology powering the Simulations. Notably, base reality exists external to all Simulations and seems not accessible by the orthogonal time pathways.

What is more, PKD specifically talks about how visiting adjacent Simulations manifests as memories and how alterations to a running Simulation feel like *déjà vu*. In the universe of *The Matrix* (the source material), anytime PKD's Programmer introduces a change to a simulated reality, which change manifests in the Simulation(s) as a glitch or *déjà vu*. PKD does not expand on how a glitch ripples across a single Simulation. He does not explain how the inhabitants perceive the change to their Simulation or how a change propagates across all Simulations running on the machine. However, we supply some insights into these questions in upcoming chapters.

While some may view the idea that we inhabit a Simulation or computer-generated program as strange, the idea itself is not as strange as the Simulations being identical except for flipped details such as who won WWII. This part of PKD's idea comes across as if the Programmer is working through scenarios as if to understand the set of all outcomes. An infinity is strongly implied.

With all that said, PKD did leave us to wonder about several details. These missing details are additional, albeit unspoken, clues. For instance, *what* is the Simulation at various levels of human experience- the Universal, the Social, and the Individual? In other words, what is the relation between humans and Simulation in these cases? As well, how is *what is Simulation* at those levels of resolution *simulated?* This detail is equal parts substrate and mediatory functionality of the substrate. Finally, for as much as PKD emphasized orthogonal time, he did not expand on the question of time being Simulation. Put differently, the notion that Simulations interlink through orthogonal time does not reveal anything about *when* in the base reality or how the Programmer experiences such.

Fortunately, these details form the basis for the artifacts we discuss throughout this work. Nevertheless, there are two more foundation sources to incorporate into our developing conceptual framework prior to moving into the scheme for those artifacts. We may also take a slight detour to flesh out essential definitions.

§1.3 The Bostrom Paper

Foremost, it is important to recognize the *A Glitch in the Matrix* documentary followed on the heels of the now famous Bostrom paper[3] in which the author asserted a probabilistic argument for the claim that we inhabit a computer-generated Simulation. To be fair, Bostrom did not conclude that we *do* live in a Simulation. Rather, he argued it is *probable* that we do.

The probability Bostrom asserts is rooted in two of three hypotheses being false. Foremost, the Simulation Hypothesis being probable relies on the premise that civilization has reached ample technological maturity to build reality-like Simulations. Secondly, any civilization having the capability to produce Simulations then must choose to pursue their construction. Where those are true, the probability is: We are in a Simulation.

An important but overlooked detail from Bostrom's work is the suspicion that the Simulation need not be perfect (i.e., complete). In simpler terms, the entirety of reality need not be a Simulation. Rather, the Simulation is only the part of reality we inhabit and can perceive at any given time. Consequently, we must consider whether our perception of the immediate natural world must be false for a Simulation

---

[3] Bostrom, N. (2003). Are we living in a computer Simulation? *The philosophical quarterly*, 53(211), 243-255.

Hypothesis to be true. In other words, "Is the Simulation Hypothesis exclusive?" might be a good framing of the inquiry. According to the argument, limited rendering would be a plausible optimization strategy for a capable civilization but not necessarily a strategy that makes Simulation exclusive.

In fact, modern video games and virtual reality technologies constrain draw distance and object rendering. Constraining draw distance and object rendering reduces the processing load on the underlying machine. However, the Simulation Hypothesis supplies an added or alternative explanation since the Programmer or Machine in base reality needs to deploy updates to the Simulation. Thus, the Programmer can implement these updates behind the scenes where the Machine is not currently rendering the Simulation. In other words, the imperfection of reality might be part of the Simulation's perfection.

§1.4 The Philosophical Background of Simulation Theory

The thinking found in the following four philosophers is capable of sufficiently characterizing the philosophical background of Simulation Theory: Plato (428/7 – 348/347) BC, Descartes (1596-1650), Deleuze (1925-1995), and Baudrillard (1929-2007).[4] Though it should also be noted that because Simulation Theory asks questions regarding the reality of existence, the framework of existentialism adds additional questions regarding *constraints* and *transcendence* in Simulation Theory. That being said, all of these philosophies will be discussed in the section below to which they are most relevant.

---

[4] Since this book is focused on Simulation theory, rather than the work of these philosophers, the discussion of these philosophers will not be exhaustive; however, at the same time, the work of other philosophers will also be mentioned, so as to help readers situate both the work of the philosophers and the discussion of Simulation theory. To that end, we will also mention the work of Martin Heidegger (1889-1976), Jacques Ellul (1912-1994), Louis Marin (1931-1992), and Theodore J. Kaczynski (1942-).

Plato is famously known to distinguish between a higher dimension, which includes the Platonic Forms and the Transcendentals, and a lower, carnal, and erotic, material dimension. That distinction is a binary opposition, and whenever you have a binary opposition with one of the sides privileged over the other, then there is potential for one of the opposites to be a Simulation of the other. Put more concretely, if there are only so many (existentially relevant) Platonic Forms and Ideas, only so many archetypes, then the dimension in which those forms, ideas, and archetypes are physically instantiated may be a physical Simulation of those forms, ideas, and archetypes. One dimension is real (what we, in general, call *base reality*) and the other dimension is not real in the same way.

René Descartes is popularly known as a *substance dualist*, and of those two substances, the mental and the physical, the being to which his famous *cogito ergo sum* (I think, therefore, I am) points is mental and, ontologically, subjective. Thus, whereas Plato's philosophy is wider in its scope of application, Descartes' philosophy is the background of thinking regarding the subject in relation to Simulation. However, Descartes' philosophy is *not* the most philosophically accurate characterization of the subject. For that we would need to invoke the thinking of Kant and the Existentialists. Yet, for the former reasons, Descartes' philosophy must be grappled with when understanding Simulation Theory.

As a transcendental philosopher, Gilles Deleuze has an egalitarian ontology, he does not privilege one *substance* over its opposite. Rather, Deleuze's primary importance for Simulation Theory comes from his discussion of *control*. It is, of course, not mere coincidence that in *The Matrix* Morpheus says to Neo, "What is the Matrix? [It is] Control. The Matrix is a computer-generated dream world built to keep us under control."

Lastly, many people forget that Jean Baudrillard represents the avowed and explicit philosophical origin of *The Matrix*. That's why in the *Follow the White Rabbit* scene the stash book Neo opens is Baudrillard's *Simulacra and Simulation*. In fact, Baudrillard is the best philosophical background for discussing the origin of Simulations and the difference between a base reality and a Simulation.

In sum, though the writings of all four (4) of these philosophers help us gain insights regarding Simulation Theory, the work of these philosophers tends to naturally divide across what in Section Three, just below, we explain as *levels of resolution* in Simulation Theory. In this way, Plato's writings may be most helpful for understanding what we call *Actual Simulation*, Deleuze's and Baudrillard's writings may be most helpful for understanding *Virtual Simulation*, and Descartes' writings may be most helpful for understanding *Mental Simulation*. Similarly, the Universal, Social, and Individual levels of resolution follow the same pattern, Plato, Deleuze and Baudrillard, and Descartes, respectively.

This is not a statement against the many uses you can find of the writings of these philosophers across all of Simulation Theory. Rather, the logic of Simulation Theory drives the approach in this book. The work is more than just noting interesting connections between philosopher writings and Simulation Theory. Our hope is to explicate the logical structure of Simulation Theory, so that readers can understand, and navigate it, in a coherent way. To that end, the writings of Plato, Deleuze and Baudrillard, and Descartes, respectively, best illuminate the levels of resolution found in Simulation Theory.

§2 Key Definitions

§2.1 Simulation and Simulation Theory

The meaning of *Simulation* and *Simulation Theory* in the source material varies. For instance, while Philip K. Dick refers to *alternate presents*, the *Glitch* documentary (in one segment) demonstrates Simulation in the form of a programmed reality, Minecraft. Thus, clarity in how we use these terms is paramount.

A helpful place to start may be Barry Francis Dainton's definition of *Simulation*, that is, "any state or episode of consciousness is to be regarded as simulated if it is produced by non-standard methods in a controlled fashion."[5] First, we take *non-standard* to mean either a synthetic mind emerging from a physical, embodied brain or a synthetic mind-brain structure.

Second, we interpret "controlled" in a standard consciousness to imply the mind is, at least, not fully in control of itself. That is, a standard mind cannot manifest itself into a non-mind state and the substrate – barring any trauma or biochemical induced alteration – cannot control the mind either. Here, the mind (software) and substrate (hardware) are often indistinguishable. Notice, then, that Simulation Theory invokes ideas of free will and control.

Further, staying within the Cartesian mind/body context of Dainton's definition, then we may note, conversely, that while a "non-standard" mind may not have directional control over its substrate, the substrate certainly can affect a synthetic mind. Put another way, this is software running on borrowed hardware with an unseen actor in control.

Beyond a Cartesian mind/body context, a Simulation exists in contrast with what it is not. Thus, there is a natural distinction between a Simulation and base reality. There are several types of Simulation. Each differs in the way it instantiates a *Simulation*. These categories of Simulation Theory are the *Actual*, the *Virtual*, and the *Mental*. Further, as an alternative to a Cartesian dualistic approach, emphasizing consciousness, we will also take a more phenomenological approach contrasting between different types of *worlds*, that is, the *Um-welt*, *Mit-welt*,

---

[5] Dainton, Barry Francis. (2002). Innocence Lost: Simulation Scenarios: Prospects and Consequences. (p. 2).

Selbst-welt, and *Eigen-welt* – that which physically surrounds us, our participation in the *with-world* or (social) relations to other beings, our relation to ourself (specifically as a body), and our relation to spirituality or Be-ing itself.

This distinction allows us to envision how each of those worlds – or *Welts* of the *Welt*-matrix – may be simulated or a Simulation. To say that we live in a Simulation, then, is understood as a Simulation Hypothesis. Further, to provide an account of how it is that we live in a Simulation, or how we came to live in a Simulation, is understood as a Simulation Argument. The totality of how Simulation Hypotheses and Simulation Arguments relate to one another is understood as Simulation Theory.

Thus, Simulation Theory includes the examination of the finite number of ways the term "Simulation" may be understood. In this way, Simulation Theory includes all of the different Simulation Hypotheses related to the different understandings of Simulation and all the Simulation Arguments used to defend Simulation Hypotheses.

The goal of this book is not to reach conclusions regarding any particular Simulation Hypothesis or Argument. That is to say, the goal of this book is not to answer the central question of Simulation Theory, "Do we live in a simulation?" Rather, the goal of this book is to enumerate and explicate the possible kinds of Simulation. What *Simulation* can mean if it is true that we are living in a Simulation. Though some terms may be understood differently depending on the context – philosophical or computational – where they are used. We have exerted effort to clarify key terminology.

§2.2 Virtualization

The term *virtualization* appears throughout the documentary *A Glitch in the Matrix* while also being pervasive in popular information technology culture. Depending on your frame of reference, "the Simulation" might be synonymous with "virtualization." At the same time, virtualization may be a foreign concept for some. Therefore, on the one hand, it is important to explicitly define how virtualization is situated in the framework of Simulation Theory.

On the other hand, it is important to disambiguate "virtualization" and "virtual reality." Thus, it is helpful to distinguish two meanings of "virtualization" – the philosophical and the computational. To be addressed below, these two meanings naturally have a relation to the set of "what and how" interrogatives we employ to examine Simulation Theory. Whereas "virtual reality" coincides with the "what," *virtualization* coincides with the "how." Section 3.2, below, will further clarify the "what," so this section will now further clarify the "how."

Given this potential to confuse the "what" and "how," we will name the "whats" here, for the sake of differentiating them from the "hows." All the possible meanings of the term "Simulation," fit into three general categories. Thus, there are three types of Simulation: Actual-Type (1), Virtual-Type (1.5), and Mental-Type (2).

The numbers regarding these types may help us remember that these three types are nested and move toward greater abstraction. In other words, answers to the "What kind of Simulation is being discussed?" move from the Actual to the Mental, and, in regard to the "how," that movement represents a trajectory of *virtualization*. Hence, the difference between "virtual" (as in virtual reality) and "virtualization." What is more, this trajectory of increasing abstraction may also be understood in terms of the relation the virtualization process has to its (underlying) hardware substrate.[6] Thus, each of the three types of virtualization correspond to techniques for abstracting a computing system from its underlying hardware.

---

[6] "Underlying" here also means "ontologically prior." In other words, in the Actual Type of Simulation, the actual hardware is ontologically prior to its virtualization. The process of virtualization depends on its substrate for its existence.

In other words, with each type of virtualization along the trajectory of increasing abstraction, from Actual to Mental, the relation between the location of the programs we use and the operating system differs. This is actually intuitive and straightforward, if we consider that: As the extent to which a Simulation is abstract and nested increases, so does the extent to which its functionality may be nested in software, rather than hardware. For instance, the existence of a Mental Simulation may depend on a level of virtualization which itself depends on a level of hardware.

More precisely stated, in the vocabulary of computer science, what varies across the three techniques for abstracting a computing system from its underlying hardware is the relation of a substrate to the kernel[7] of an operating system. Tying this all together is the concept of a hypervisor. Importantly, then, a hypervisor is the technology powering virtualization and acts as a type of kernel. Distinguishing between the types of virtualization indicates at what level the hypervisor is to be found. In turn, the kind of hypervisor involved dictates to what degree the associated hardware and software are abstracted layers collectively powering a system.

In modern computing, virtualization is a way to run multiple computing systems on a single hardware platform or substrate. The virtualized computing systems are *virtual machines*. Despite existing entirely as software, these virtual machines are just as functionally real as the hardware computer running them. Thus, there are three degrees of realness pertaining to computing power[8] and performance.

The first type of virtualization is Type 1. This virtualization involves replacing a typical kernel with a kernel-level hypervisor. The kernel-level hypervisor performs

---

[7] A **kernel** is a program serving as the core or heart of a computing system. The kernel has complete control over both the hardware below it as well as the software above it.

[8] Computing power is understood as the number of calculations per second a computer can perform.

virtualization directly. The second type of virtualization is Type 1.5 and represents a modification to a normal kernel with a hypervisor module. The third type of virtualization is Type 2. This type of virtualization positions the hypervisor substrate alongside other software running in an operating system.

Roughly speaking, a Type 2 virtualization has limited computing power and performance because it is instantiated within the user's context in the base operating system. In contrast, a Type 1 virtualization has few limitations because it is instantiated directly atop the hardware substrate (i.e., bare metal). There are a variety of reasons why one might use one or the other (or Type 1.5) but those are outside the scope of this book. What is material is that the types represent a different capacity and capability to produce simulated computation.

For completeness, we should note that a sufficiently powerful base computer can perform *nested* virtualization. In other words, a virtualized kernel can run a further virtualized kernel. At each step, the virtualization is proportionally more constrained, but it will work.

Lastly, in regard to degrees of realness just noted, virtualized objects are nonetheless real, or at least suitably real, as to be indistinguishable from an identical non-virtualized object. While the present-day implementation of virtualization is not sufficient to simulate anything beyond a computer or application it certainly serves as a conceptual reference. Further, it should be clear now how the concept of virtualization – as a response to the "how" question – differs from the concept of the virtual – as a response to the "what" question, regarding virtual reality.

§2.3 Rendering

Rendering is a term commonly found regarding graphic design. In other words, we place files, which may – philosophically – be understood as elements, into a final composition, and then, that composition gets rendered.

Thus, "rendering" refers to the process of creating self-contained files viewable outside of the program rendering them. This is outside of where such files exist as elements.

The computational notion of *rendering* is more general. A graphics processing unit (GPU) renders a user interface and projects the interface through output to a monitor screen. GPUs also render scenes within a video game. Rendering is not just graphics in computation though. *Rendering is a conversion of bit values into an output stream.* The modern computing interface is graphical however and has created a strong association between computational rendering and graphical output.

Rendering is also a term found in regard to performance art. For example, notice how the term rendering relates to the term *rendition*. When a symphony or a band plays a composition, the composition includes elements or distinct parts of music, and the performance of the composition is a particular rendering of the composition. One musical group's rendition of a composition may be different from another.

Therefore, "rendering" is a key term for Simulation Theory, right along with the terms "Simulation," "base reality," and "virtualization." If we are living in a Simulation, the Simulation – at any given instance of experiencing it – would be a rendered instantiation of all the potential ways its elements could have been composed. In other words, living in a Simulation means experiencing a rendered Simulation.

Finally, the term rendering is quite helpful in illuminating an essential distinction. Section 3 below describes these types in more detail. However, the essential distinction can be stated here.

On the one hand, in an Actual type of Simulation, because base reality and the Simulation are indistinguishable, the hypervisor rendering the Simulation must be either located outside of the Simulation, or, along the lines of Bostrom's

Simulation Argument, using the rendering as a kind of mask. In other words, the part we experience as real-time Simulation may only be a portion of the base reality in which the hypervisor is located. On the other hand, because base reality may be distinguished from the Simulation regarding both Virtual and Mental types of Simulation, the hypervisor rendering the Simulation will be located in either base reality or the Simulation. Though this distinction may not seem essential at this point, its value will be apparent by the end of the book.

§3 How This Book Is Organized: Levels of Resolution and Types of Simulation

§3.1 Levels of Resolution

When you ask the question, "Are we living in a Simulation?" it is *impossible* to determine a correct answer before knowing what is meant by the term "Simulation." On the one hand, there are several definitions for the term *Simulation.* On the other, these definitions have an internal logic to them. That is, they imply their own essential ordering.

The levels of resolution span three types of Simulation: the Actual, the Virtual, and the Mental. In fact, the types of Simulation may also be thought of as levels of resolution. All these terms have a deep philosophical history, but for now we simply need to remember the levels of resolution occupy a trajectory of increasing abstraction. An Actual Simulation is more all-encompassing than a Mental Simulation. This distinction between levels of resolution also helps us see that it is possible to use the artifacts discovered evidencing one level of resolution to draw conclusions about a different level of resolution.

In this way, the distinction helps us keep track whenever evidence which could only pertain to Virtual Simulation suggests the truth of Actual Simulation. Evidence from one level of resolution does not necessarily pertain to another level of resolution.

Once we know the level of resolution, then we know what *genera* of meaning we are to understand. Next, we can further *specify* each level of resolution in terms of a grouping of persons or selection of reality. Thus, each level of resolution divides into Universal, Social, and Individual. Just like the genera, these terms also imply their own internal ordering. Which is to say, the Universal is the most all-encompassing, and the Individual is the least. The universal necessarily includes the Individual, but the Individual does not necessarily include the Universal.

Finally, specifying each level of resolution in terms of Universal, Social, and Individual determines the three essential meanings of each level of resolution. When a person uses the term *Simulation*, they could mean Actual reality, and they could mean it, Universally, in terms of *all* of Actual reality, just the Social (e.g., human, sentient, however we wish to characterize *Social*), or just the Individual. The Individual's not being the level of the Social shows that though Simulation may be true regarding an individual of a species or social group, it need not be true of every member of that species or social group. Later, we refer to this as "Morpheus' Distinction." Of course, if Actual Universal Simulation were meant, then it would necessarily include all the individuals of a species, despite any differences illuminated from the point of view of the difference between the Individual and the Social.

Moreover, recalling that Simulation Types are nested, like the focusing of a camera, resolution is continuous but consistent across all its levels. Roughly speaking, we can imagine changing the focus on a camera lens so that more or less of a background object is observable compared to an object in the foreground. In this manner, we can say there is a graduated change from one level of resolution to another. Objects incrementally move in and out of focus in relation to our observation of those objects. At the same time, we observe all objects in the frame equally in the picture despite their placement in the activated field of resolution.

A grid, or matrix, best illustrates these distinctions.

Simulation Theory
Levels of Resolution
The Spectrum ↛
(a) Actual Simulation
Universal
Social
Individual
(b) Virtual Simulation
Universal
Social
Individual
(c) Mental Simulation
Universal
Social
Individual

Table 1 – Artifacts of Simulation Theory organized in levels of resolution

Just to be clear, a few illustrations may be helpful. When asked the question, *do we live in a Simulation*, it could be meant in terms of the level of the Mental, specifically, the Individual level of the Mental. Meant that way, the question would be asking if we think that some person's – some, one, individual's – mind is in a Simulation. Thus, it could mean a Simulation traps one individual's mind or that the one individual's experience of having a mind is not really the experience of having a mind (like the other individuals in a society or in existence), but, rather, it is the experience of a simulated mind. Likewise, Simulation could refer to the Actual level, and, specifically, the Universal resolution of the Actual level. Meant that way, the question would be asking if everything that is experienced as reality is taking place in a Simulation; is everything we take to be real a Simulation?

As a last illustration, the Virtual, Social, level of resolution may be meant by Simulation. Meant that way, the question would be asking if living in a society itself or some form(s) of society constitute living in a Simulation. In other words, not everyone and not just one person; rather, forms governing some individuals in society may be artifacts of a kind of Simulation.[9] In this fashion, the levels of resolution are a type of roadmap for both the remaining sections of this chapter as well as the artifacts we aim to render as guide stones useful for interpreting Simulation Theory.

§3.2 Types of Simulation: Actual, Virtual, and Mental

The first position and associated artifacts we evaluate in this book concerns *Actual Simulation.*

We start here because Actual Simulation is the most literal interpretation of the possibilities. Further, Actual Simulation covers inhabiting a Simulation most broadly while carrying forward the narrowest outcomes. If we take Simulation Theory to imply that we inhabit an Actual Simulation, we can use the following series of questions to reveal the underlying logic associated with such an interpretation.

The first question we can ask is, *what is Actual Simulation at the level of resolution of the universe?* This question drives at the meaning of reality insofar as existence itself is an Actual Simulation. There is no base reality to which participants in the Simulation can transcend. Thus, to the inhabitants of an Actual Simulation, *everything* is part of the Simulation. This is indeed the literal interpretation of Simulation in Simulation Theory, at least as far as popular, mainstream culture, perceives the idea.

If we take a slightly narrower focus, the question becomes, *what is Actual Simulation at the level of resolution of the Social?* When we consider Actual Simulation in relation to the Social, the resolution scales down from the Universal context discussed above, from the universe to society. An Actual Social Simulation, then, refers to society as a

---

[9] The term *beings* may also be substituted for *persons*, then theories articulated in terms of multiple civilizations, even those articulated in terms of alien races, would still fit into these levels of resolution. In fact, such theories would fit into the Actual and Social (societal – multiple individuals) level of resolution.

Simulation without a base reality to which someone in such a Simulation can transcend. A point to consider in the Social resolution is the Simulation does not have to render everything nor render what is within the scope of the Simulation but not known by the perceiver (recall constraints draw distance and object rendering noted above).

Thirdly, at the narrowest scope, we can ask, *what* is Actual Simulation at the level of resolution of the Individual? Here, we are positing that Simulation occurs where consciousness, or better said the awareness of being a conscious person, manifests.

Fair warning now because the next three questions may seem repetitive because the semantic difference is subtle with changing from *what* questions to *how* inquiries. However, the difference is material to our understanding of the artifacts associated with the types of Simulation possible. Put simply, the transition takes us from inquiring about the underlying nature of the Simulation to reflecting on the mechanics of its function. Of course, we can examine how these mechanics function at all three levels of resolution – Universal, Social, and Individual.

In addition to what and how, we can ask *when* the Actual Simulation is in relation to the same three levels of resolution. Working with time, or more appropriately the perception of simulated time, allows for a triangulation of sorts. While triangulation is not necessary, it does supply a means to arrange and rearrange the artifacts to suit our growing understanding.

PKD's theory of orthogonal time hints at some overarching and fixed timeline. If we read between the lines a bit, we can take a point on the overarching timeline such as WWII and say that all Simulations must contain that point albeit *when* is flexible. Moreover, within each Simulation, all participants would be interacting with the timepoint fully and equally. In other words, there is no intermediary layer. This would be a Universal resolution of when.

Introduction

At the level of Social resolution, if society itself is the instantiation of a type of Simulation, then regarding the "when," it may be the case that a future, a past, or an orthogonally-instantiated Actual base reality may be responsible for generating our Social Simulation. Crucially, it may not be possible to know how one society relates to another in terms of which, if any, occupies base reality.

Meanwhile, Individual resolution suggests Actual Simulation is instantiated in relation to the singular person. Thus, when we consider Simulation Theory in this context, the salient point becomes the individual as both the focus of the Actual Simulation as well as the proxied source of the Simulation. In other words, the Actual Simulation is discretely bound to the individual.

From the source material, Bostrom most aptly correlates with Actual Simulation. A physical substrate denotes the Simulation runs on what technologists would refer to as bare metal. Whereas with an Actual Simulation, base reality is inaccessible to participants in the Simulation, the relationship between a Virtual Simulation and base reality is quite intuitive via analogy. It may be understood as "the difference between the map and the territory," respectively.

Virtual Simulation is a subset of Actual Simulation. Being a subset does not imply that Virtual Simulation is somehow inferior- not as real. Likewise, we should not take it to mean Virtual Simulation requires Actual Simulation. Instead, imagine Virtual Simulation as being akin to a video game. Or, as Dainton (2002) suggests, "...a life (or part of a life) is virtual rather than real if it is entirely composed of simulated experiences" (p. 2).

We suspect that most of us have at least a fuzzy idea of what *virtual reality* is; the almost real like video gaming experience requiring us to wear special goggles or headsets (like the person on the cover of this book). Additionally, immersive video gaming experiences such as Minecraft, World of Warcraft, and Elder Scrolls Skyrim have left an indelible mark on society as *virtual worlds*.

Curiously, virtual worlds such as these exist in two states. There is the state whereby the virtual world exists, say in software code, but is not instantiated. Then, virtual worlds have a state resulting from the instantiation of that software code onto a suitable substrate. The application of computer programming analogy here is proper given this is the language expressed in the Philip K. Dick and *The Matrix* foundational material.

Methodologically, the same set of *what, how,* and *when* questions may be used to bring forth Artifacts of the Simulation across all the types, and levels of resolution, constituting Simulation Theory. Fundamentally, in terms of Computer Science, the shift across these types and levels of resolution is a difference of (what) Simulation fidelity, (how) Simulation substrate, (when) experience of repetition, and change, within the Simulation and time.

The Matrix intimates a Virtual Simulation with a virtualized substrate. Base reality is actual, the Simulation into which humans are "plugged" is Virtual, and the experience of existing has been virtualized by the machines such that those humans (still) "plugged in" live in a Virtual Simulation. The movie uniquely posits that humans are singular, and the Actual and Virtual parts of reality are nested (and, in the case of Neo, can affect one another).

As well, we cannot ignore the mountain of interrelationship between modern video games and the idea of Virtual Simulation. Without doubt, a significant amount of evidence in *A Glitch in the Matrix* appears to stem from immense realism in present-day graphics processing[10] and the advent of true *virtual reality* immersion.

Mental Simulation is a subset of Virtual Simulation. On one hand, it may not be reaching to describe consciousness itself as a Mental Simulation. On the other hand, we can understand the thematization of sensory-experience as

---

[10] NVIDIA demo: https://blogs.nvidia.com/blog/2021/08/09/siggraph-research-real-time-graphics/

governed by forms instantiating a Mental Simulation. Thus, consciousness relative to specific kinds of "Mental Formation" may be understood as constituting a Simulation.

From an empirical point of view, grey matter localizes consciousness. However, we do not know what the specific properties of grey matter are such that it is a unique substrate for consciousness (cf. Chalmers, 2022). We also do not have a firm grasp of what consciousness is per se; at the same time, consciousness is awareness resulting from the unification of sensory perception. In terms of virtualization, it may be possible to compartmentalize thinking into discrete sub-thinking spaces as it were or *nested virtualizations*. This goes beyond the compartmentalization naturally arising from the sub-thinking spaces we refer to as consciousness and subconsciousness (cf. Dorpat, 1996). Furthermore, these sub-thinking spaces exist in a decoupled state relative to grey matter specifically and the nervous system in general.

Like Actual Simulation and Virtual Simulation, we can consider the levels of Simulation resolution in sets of *what*, *how*, and *when* interrogatives. Moreover, we again see more difference in the fidelity of the Simulation, a change in the nature of the Simulation substrate, as well as alterations to the experience of repetition and change within the Simulation. Time, or more succinctly the experience of time, also takes on a new form in Mental Simulation.

As we will see, the ontological and solipsistic aspects of Descartes' philosophy exemplify Simulation Theory as Mental Simulation. Transcendental phenomenology's concept of the *Welt*-Matrix functions as an alternative to mind-body binary opposition. The virtual *Welts*/worlds resulting from the thematization of sensory experience may be more or less Simulations, more or less potential mechanisms by which humans could be "plugged into" a Simulation.

Chapter 1: Actual Simulation

Dr. Pittman

Actual Simulation is a literal interpretation of the idea that we inhabit a simulated reality. The false reality is a deliberately programmed output of a machine. Furthermore, Actual Simulation implies there is one base reality, one machine capable of generating a Simulation of reality, and a single simulated reality.

To me, the most convenient and rational means to interpret the artifacts of Simulation Theory is to employ basic Set Theory. We alluded to this in the Introduction when discussing groups or sets of numbers. Further, if we use a Set Theory framework, the idea that Actual Simulation implies a one-to-one relationship between the machine and the Simulation becomes a novel focal point. Thus, we can imagine Actual Simulation to function as a first-order subset insofar as the Simulation is a faithful, one-to-one image of base reality.

On a side note, a set of things is in fact its own subset. This may seem strange because I am implying that a singular thing is in fact two things: itself and a copy (of sorts) of itself. If all the elements in the copy also exist in the source, the copy is a subset of the source. If the source has elements not in the copy, the copy is a *proper* subset. From there, we only need to document the artifacts of the Simulation according to our levels of resolution. I suggest this is best accomplished by discussing the fidelity, substrate, experience of repetition and change, and time function of Actual Simulation within each artifact level of resolution.

§1 Actual Simulation: Universal Level of Resolution

Stated simply, I think a Universal level of Actual Simulation implies that the Universal set is what is simulated for the inhabitants of the Simulation. Meaning, all things in Actual Simulation exist, in the same form, in base reality. Such things may exist in form or as an instruction for their creation. More concretely, interaction with anything and everything within the scope of the universe is taking part in the Simulation. This is a crucial point. It means that a Simulation is an instantiated, full model of reality, a Simulation of not just something that exists in base reality but all the things in base reality.

The logical question to address is *how is a Universal Actual Simulation simulated?*

§1.1 How?

Foremost, we can infer that anything outside of this Universal set is external to the Simulation. For certain, base reality is external and, in the context of Actual Simulation, not itself simulated. I do not see how an outer Actual-Universal Simulation might hold a nested Actual Simulation within. In fact, the logical constraints on such nesting would be such that the sophistication of the Actual Simulation at a Universal level of resolution would not be able to render in full detail. The compute resources available from base reality to any derivative simulated realities would be too constrained.

We can infer artifacts of Actual Simulation in this context because the question of how an Actual Simulation manifests at the Universal level of resolution is really an inquiry into the substrate and fidelity expressed in the Simulation. In all fairness, we must assume the available computing power of the base reality machine and available energy are sufficient to produce the Actual Simulation.

On one hand, a Universal level of Actual Simulation is the most substrate independent. Any object capable of computation, given enough energy and compute power, ought to be capable of generating a Universal Simulation. Yet on the other hand, once the Simulation is instantiated, there is a tight coupling between substrate and Simulation. So much so in fact, the two might not be separable.

We can surmise the substrate is capable of computation. While the substrate need not be silicon as is our current 21st century computing machines, it certainly must be capable of executing a processing function which accepts input and produces output. Within the function are the computational rules, procedures, and processes to map base reality constructs to Universal Actual Simulation constructs.

As mentioned in the opening of this chapter, the mapping or relation, between base reality and the Simulation is one-to-one. We can delve deeper into this concept now as it is the substrate acting as the relation function. Consider the following visualization (Fig. 1).

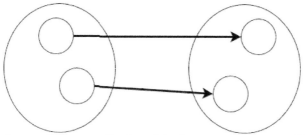

Fig. 1: A one-to-one relationship between base reality and an Actual-Universal Simulation

Furthermore, because we are dealing with the Actual Simulation type, the substrate capable of producing such Simulation, more especially at the Universal level of resolution, would be unique to the companion Simulation. Thus, for example, if the base reality universe has two machines running two different Simulations, the two substrates mediating between machine and Simulation would necessarily be different. In other words, the substrate for a given Simulation is the substrate for that Simulation and only that Simulation.

Finally, it is easy to assume the machine in base reality is in fact a singular entity. This need not be the case. The machine could be a collective of machines otherwise known as a cluster. Likewise, there could of course be more than a machine producing a Simulation. If the language here is confusing, just remember that the relation between machine and Simulation is one-to-one. Alternatively, we can picture a zero-dimensional object (i.e., a dot) as representative of the Machine-Simulation relationship.

Regardless of the arrangement of the machine singleton, a direct handoff from the Simulation substrate is the virtualization layer. Because virtualization can vary in kind and degree across the Simulation types and levels of resolution, we should lend effort to discovering important artifacts related to Actual-Universal Simulation.

I think of virtualization as a step forward in the answer to *how is the Simulation* simulated. This is the layer between the Machine and the instantiated Simulation. Another way to conceptualize virtualization is to look at it as the computational object bootstrapped by the substrate. Further, we can view virtualization as the computational object receiving output from the Simulation Function in the Machine.

Leveraging the language from our discussion in the Introduction, we can describe the type of virtualization. I would refer to Actual Simulation at the Universal level of resolution as fundamentally a Type 1 virtualization. The substrate serves as the hypervisor kernel. Put differently, the hypervisor is not separate from the substrate. Meanwhile, the Simulation runs directly atop the hypervisor with no middleware between the two.

A valid critique of this idea might point out that virtualization is not necessary if the Machine is more-or-less directly loading the Simulation. While true, I think virtualization makes sense to use if we consider related ideas such as containment, disaster recovery, longevity, and so forth.

Furthermore, as we look towards *what is Simulation*, I think we must also contemplate how the Machine selects details and elements from base reality as input, loads them into the Simulation Function. The same inquiry is possible when considering the link from the substrate to virtualization, provided as output into the Actual-Universal Simulation.

Because the base reality Machine virtualizes Actual Simulation directly, without middleware there is no input or output filtering at the Universal level of resolution. The Machine simply pipes input to the Simulation Function. Then, Simulation Function injects its output into a virtualization runtime[11] as the de facto Simulation.

Fair enough, but how the Machine encapsulates base reality as input matters to us. To understand this point we must peek ahead and see artifacts such as variance, repetition, and error, as well as fidelity form a picture of *what* is Simulation. It is this mechanism which defines those artifacts. Thus, if the simulated universe is a one-to-one instantiation of base reality, the possibility for deviated values across those artifacts will reflect such.

So, the Machine cannot select base reality universe element by element, piece by piece. Instead, the Machine must use the entirety of base reality universe as a single input. This has computational merit insofar as processing fewer, larger inputs is more efficient than processing numerous, smaller inputs. An approximation of how this might work is to think about the input as a snapshot. Then, because there are no filters on the output either, the Machine injects or superimposes the base reality universe snapshot into the virtualization layer.

---

[11] I use runtime here to encapsulate all the computational components necessary to run the Simulation. In computing terms, this is both hardware and software. Taken as action, runtime is the point at which a program loads into memory and becomes available to the process or user instantiating it.

§1.2 What?

Carrying forward from the *how*, I want to discuss the *what* aspect of Actual-Universal Simulation. *What* is interesting because it gives us hints as to what to look at once the Simulation is running. Put simply, because of the substrate and fidelity of the Actual Simulation case, we should expect that the Simulation holds all details and elements from base reality.

I use *all* because I suspect there cannot be any rearrangement of these details and elements. The make and manner of the Actual Simulation must be universally consistent with base reality. Nothing more, nothing less. One way to describe this in more detail is with the concept of variance.

In an Actual Simulation at the Universal level of resolution, instantiations of the Simulation ought to show little, if any, variance. To conceptualize this properly, imagine an Actual Simulation- version 1.0 let's call it- runs for one billion years. Further imagine the Simulation records, catalogs, and indexes all activity within itself. If another Simulation, version 2.0, runs for another billion years, upon comparison we would find the set of activities between the Simulations not just highly similar but dead drop identical. Again, because we are working at the Universal resolution, this *must* be true down to the subatomic level.

Interestingly, I suspect variance in this regard would be observable from outside of the Simulation. The observation could be from the perspective of the Machine, the Programmer, or all base reality. In parallel, I don't think variance would be observable from within the Simulation. The Actual-Universal Simulation would not have any connection to prior Simulations to anything or anyone existing within it.

Conversely, as glitches factor heavily into the source material, we can interpret unexpected events or unexplainable phenomena to be evidence of change in the

Simulation. Principally, a change or update would be an alteration of degree to a fundamental rule or law. Thus, any effects would be universal, broadly affecting the entire Simulation and everything within it. However, I doubt such change would be noticeable even if it did occur in Actual Simulation at the level of Universal resolution.

I think this is a sound position because of the way the Actual-Universal Simulation is instantiated from a snapshot of base reality. If we presuppose any update occurs similarly, which it would since the Simulation Function has not changed, then the entire state of the Simulation would change at once. This includes the observer within the Simulation as well as the relation between the observer and the Simulation. In other words, there would not be a delta to show change had occurred. Similarly, repetition within the Simulation would be universal-global.

Broadly speaking, we can take *fidelity* to be the exactness of the Simulation compared to base reality. Fidelity is useful as part of our response to *how* the Machine generates the Simulation. Fidelity which allows us to differentiate between what the Machine should simulate and what the Machine does simulate. Propositionally, if the substrate is the Simulation Function, we can conceptualize fidelity as the Simulation fabric.

With that in mind, because of the Actual-Universal substrate coupling, the fidelity of a Universal Actual Simulation would be utterly indistinguishable from base reality. The Simulation Function outputs precisely and accurately based on input. The instantiation would be lossless. Computationally, this seems plausible since the input of either a thing in base reality or the instruction to generate the thing is a one-to-one function and the substrate is working as a translator of sorts. With that said, we can explore the fidelity of the Actual Simulation at this resolution more technically through the characteristics of resolution, error and accuracy, sensitivity, precision, and capability.

For clarity, the Machine must output a resolution granularity at least as detailed as the base reality universe. Computationally, the Simulation Function encodes the base universe into the Simulation. Encoding is simply the translation from one format to another. As a side note, I am tempted to use the term *binary* here to describe the encoding (i.e., 0 and 1 as True and False or Off and On). However, there is no reason to infer the Machine runs according to a traditional binary logic. In fact, the Machine could be running with quantum bits. Quantum bits means the Machine has more potential states than two[12]. To refer to such a Machine as binary is an oversimplification.

Concurrently, how closely the encoded elements in the Simulation match the *source* elements in base reality serve as a measure for fidelity accuracy. By *match*, I mean bit for bit identicalness since any flipped bit (i.e., a 0 where there should be a 1) is an error. For this reason, like traditional computing, there would need to be *error-correction code* (ECC) at the Machine and substrate layers. The ECC detects bit level errors and can restore the intended values from within, prior to instantiating the Simulation.

After instantiation, and from the perspective of base reality, the Programmer might have instrumentation measuring the precision of the Simulation. Here, the precision measure of fidelity is indicative of how the Simulation Function has executed the relation or mapping instructions. Since we are at the Universal level of resolution in Actual Simulation, we ought to expect perfect precision from the one-to-one mapping. Then, with that expectation met, we can move into the Simulation itself.

Fidelity is measurable within the Simulation. The Simulation expresses interconnected measures of sensitivity and capability. The former is a gauge for how

---

[12] Quantum computation is fundamentally different than classical computation. Instead of using only either the *1* or the *0* of binary at a single time (clock cycle), quantum use qubits that stand for both 0 and 1 simultaneously.

the Simulation responds to internal stimuli. Such stimuli include any action or behavior in the Simulation. These must precisely correspond to the action and behavior in base reality. Coupled with that sensitivity are the functional limits on interactions between such simulated actions or behaviors. We can encapsulate as capability.

It goes without saying such interactions would need to occur without deviation or variance based on the corresponding capability of base reality. With that said, we are missing a critical part of any Simulation type and level of resolution: time.

§1.3 When?

I think time would progress at a fixed rate in the Actual-Universal Simulation. I base this on the tight coupling between the universal rules and laws present in base reality and those in the Actual Simulation. In fact, I think time would progress at the same fixed rate between reality and Simulation. The clock in base reality and the clock in the Actual-Universal Simulation tick in unison. A second in base reality is the same second passing in the Simulation.

When the Machine *starts* the Actual Simulation would be variable. In other words, there is no reason instantiation of an Actual Simulation starting at year zero mapped to year 2018 in base reality if 2018 could not happen. In fact, the Machine could initialize the Simulation from any base reality historical point. All the moments, events, and so forth become part of the simulated universe and time would progress forward from this origin.

Again, this is representative of a one-to-one mapping between base reality and Actual Simulation reality. Further, this implies that events occur in the same order. There would be no *variance*. This strikes me as internally consistent. Likewise, the entire Actual Simulation- how, what, and when alike- is bound by a set of constraints stemming from relation between realities.

§1.4 Constraints

Any Simulation has constraints. Not all types of Simulations have the same constraints though. The constraints certainly do not manifest in the same way at various levels of resolution. Thus, I think it behooves us to work through what is meant by constraint in the context of this work.

Foremost, I don't think of constraints as limitations even though the terms are synonymous. A limitation is the end of something, the boundary past which the thing cannot expand past. Or, if the thing can expand past the boundary there will be negative consequence. In contrast, a constraint is something that must considered as a fundamental requirement for a thing to *be*. Whether any limitations apply is after the fact and is irrelevant.

Given the foundational material, we must imagine the use of *computer* by PKD and *machine* in the Matrix for example are synonymous. While any such computer or machine may not be the type of device you are reading this book on, the theory of computation is general enough to apply to both it and the Simulation generating device. The Simulation Theory Machine is a *computing device* for converting elements of base reality into Simulation. We can derive reasonable constraints because of this generality.

In general terms, the pre-existing natural laws found in base reality constrain an Actual-Universal Simulation. I think about these constraints as belonging in one of two categories: compute resources and compute operations. The former applies to running the Simulation while the latter apply to the Simulation once it is running or as pre-conditions and post-conditions, respectively.

Potentially, a simple observation undermines the concept of our universe as a computer Simulation: no machine can run a Simulation of itself for any length of time unless the machine has access to more compute resources (i.e., processing power, storage density, and available energy) than required by the instantiated Simulation. That would be the classical refutation based on our knowledge of computer science. I share the instinct as a computer scientist. So, yes, these factors would need to be available to the base reality Machine in quantities of scale slightly more than what base reality itself requires.

At face value such a proposition seems absurd. However, there may be exceptions which seem like violations of natural law. Such exceptions beg the question: how could a Simulation use more compute resources than what exists in base reality?

I think compute power, storage and energy are strict constraints. In other words, there does not appear to be a way to exceed the capacity of the base reality universe. True but we don't need to exceed the capacity of base reality. Instead, we need to instantiate the Actual-Universal Simulation in a manner requiring slightly less than the capacity of base reality. To that end, we need just enough compute power, storage, and energy to make that possible.

We can hand wave storage away if we consider compression or similar techniques. I don't think hand waving is necessary though if we are using base reality itself as the input and we accept that there may not be a need to *store* the Simulation in a persistent medium. Persistence is a safe assumption for limited features though. At a minimum, the machine must load configuration parameters (i.e., Nazi Germany winning or losing WWII) for the Simulation from somewhere. The machine may also need to reboot from time to time.

As well, the universe itself constrains and limits the total amount of storage possible. The computational perspective on this comes from the Berkenstein bound and related thermodynamics for storage. Taken at face value, the amount of storage available cannot be more than the quantity of stuff needed to build the storage. Principally, this is the same thing as not being able to build a sandcastle large than the sum of all the sand on the beach.

For energy, it would not be a stretch to imagine any civilization interested and capable of producing Actual-Universal Simulation could implement Dyson spheres[13]. A simple rule of thumb in computing is that more computation (e.g., compute power) requires more power in terms of energy. In this manner, power is a boundary constraint for the Simulation. The total energy available (a) on the planet wherein base reality exists and (b) the star powering the solar system wherein base reality exists limit available power.

Correspondingly, such a civilization could use the resultant energy resources to power computation using a massive, star-sized device called a Matrioshka Brain[14]. Regardless of how one might interpret PDK's conception of the base reality machine or even the machines or construct from *The Matrix*, compute (i.e., processing) power is a fundamental constraint too. The speed of computation in conjunction with the amount of computation occurring within a unit of speed measurement (usually *seconds*) are expressions of compute power. One applicable method to evaluate this constraint is Bremermann's processing speed limit which shows a means to give the largest computational rate relative to the size of the computational machine. Plainly, the larger the machine the higher the rate of computation available. Thus, computation on the scale of a star- a Matrioshka Brain- seems large enough to house the complexity and componentry necessary for compute power at this level.

As an aside, a machine having enough compute or processing power to simulate consciousness would have the capacity for consciousness itself. In this way, the ideas of machine and programmer expressed by PKD are the same construct. This is notable because the fabric

---

[13] A Dyson sphere is a feat of solar engineering. This is a device…, would give humanity the ability to directly harness all the energy from a star.
[14] A Matrioshka Brain is a hypothetical Class-B stellar engine.

supporting Simulation would be materially different. Some of the constraints may not be applicable. We will revisit this aside in a later chapter.

For now, we can discuss the constraints on signaling and communication between base reality, the Machine, and the Actual-Universal Simulation. In the case of Actual-Universal Simulation, the signaling and communication must be lossless and real-time without degradation. Delay, jitter, and failed sequencing would certainly cause a breakdown in the Simulation at a level whereby the Simulation crumbles.

In the context of Actual-Universal Simulation, the natural laws governing speed and reliability of the transmission medium further constrain signaling and communication. Modern computers use copper and electricity. Near-future computers might harness photons and optical pathways. Neither are immune from errors, delays, jittering, or sequencing failures. I think the builders of the Machine, its signaling and communication subsystems, would design the Simulation apparatus with the lack of immunity in mind.

As well, the Actual-Universal Simulation and Machine have interoperability and extensibility constraints. Because the Machine tightly couples the Actual Simulation to the base reality substrate, interoperability between different Machines would not be possible. As a matter of fact, I don't think the Actual-Universal Simulation, once instantiated, could run on a Machine that is not the same Machine that originated the Simulation. No swapping of hardware or software. Consequently, this implies the Machine and therefore the Simulation are not extensible. No upgrades.

To that end, when a computational object is in the state we intend, we say the object has integrity. The opposite then is the object is not in the intended state and thus has lost integrity. Another way to articulate a loss of integrity is to say the object is corrupted which is to say a 0 has become a 1 or vice-versa. For completeness, such integrity is measurable using a mathematical one-way function referred to as *hashing*[15].

I mention integrity because the Simulation Function would require a non-corrupted version of reality as input. Computationally, the Simulation generating function would need to check that input is in the expected state when received. Thus, reality integrity check is necessary. Separately, the machine would need to have an integrity checking feature for the running Simulation.

§2 Actual Simulation: Social Level of Resolution

Moving forward to the second artifact of the Simulation, we can imagine the Social level of resolution within the Actual Simulation type as a subset of the universe. In this sense, action or participation in society is participation in a Simulation. Better said, society and all its social norms, constructs, and so forth *are the Simulation.* Thus, the Social subset contains all elements necessary to instantiate society and the mechanisms necessary to interact with it.

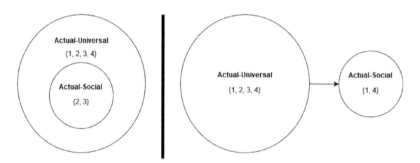

Fig. 2: Two visualizations for a Social subset

---

[15] Hashing is a mathematical function to map a computational object of any size to a value of fixed size. Specifically, I am referring to *checksum* hashing. Here, the hash or checksum of the string *Simulation* might be 1582054665. The string *Simulation* is only ever this checksum and no other string can have this specific hash ouput.

Because we are still working within the Actual Simulation type, the relation between base reality and Simulation is still one-to-one. However, unlike the Universal level of resolution where the Machine and Simulation Function map all elements from the base reality universe to the same elements in the Simulation, a Social level of resolution only requires a relation between elements necessary to construct social experience. As a result, the *how, what,* and *when* are different from, we discussed in the Universal resolution.

§2.1 How?

There are two answers to how the Machine simulates an Actual Simulation at the Social level of resolution. The first answer is the Machine uses an aperture to tune input from base reality. The aperture acts as a form of multiplexer-demultiplexer device, or it could be a signal attenuation device. In either case, the Machine would ingest only *social* level elements from base reality. The second answer involves the inner mechanisms of the Machine, the Simulation Function. Here, we again have two options: a change to the Simulation generation function in the base reality machine or a preprocessor to step-down the resolution. In either case, the substrate acts as a barrier or field with two sides.

Visualize a fence with computational abilities. On one side, the field is intermeshed into the base reality machine. The other side is the Simulation.

The substrate remains unchanged in the Social level of resolution because we cannot move beyond the tight coupling between base reality, Machine, Simulation Function, and Simulation. The coupling between substrate and Simulation is as strong as in the Universal level of resolution. The difference is the relation, and thus the coupling. is to social elements rather than universal elements. We are still working through a one-to-one mapping albeit at the Social level of resolution instead of the Universal.

Similarly, the substrate is unique to the Actual-Social Simulation. The Machine cannot share the substrate in any way. The implication, if we continue with the one-dimensional or dot conceptualization, is the Machine simulates a single social construct (i.e., society, social group, and so forth).

Using PKD's *A Man in the High Castle* for example, the Simulation is the United States of America. Well, Germany and Japan are too. This is despite the significant *social* differences from PKD's base reality. If the Programmer wished to simulate another society in the same content, that would require a different machine and a different substrate.

Be that as it may, we are still working, minimally, within the constraints of Actual Simulation. This is a subtle but significant difference that may show an alteration to the virtualization used by the base reality machine to load the Simulation instance.

Actual Simulation at the Social level resolution leads me to continue thinking of Type 1 hypervisors. The Machine directly couples the hypervisor and the substrate. This was the case in the Actual-Universal Simulation as well. Further, such direct coupling seems necessarily so because we are still in the Actual Simulation type. A change of resolution would not require- or allow for that matter- a change in underlying computational architecture.

With that being said, the difference in resolution would bring forth a change in the virtualization runtime. The difference stems from the Machine having two virtualization parts. The first part of the virtualization instantiates the Actual-Social Simulation. Another part instantiates everything not the Simulation. Both parts exist in the virtualization, but both are not in the Simulation.

For instance, imagine we are taking part in society X. The Machine simulates this society per the level of resolution. Clearly, society X exists in the universe, but the universe is not the Simulation. Instead, the universe is a Machine rendered *backdrop*, injected into the virtualization layer so that the Actual-Social Simulation has a fabric to be situated into.

I need to risk a detour at this point to flesh out what *rendering* means in the above statement. By render, I mean the Machine is employing a form of artificial intelligence called *generative adversarial network* (GAN) machine learning. Normally the GAN involves two neural networks working in tandem to generate data and then classify such data as *real* or *fake*[16]. The goal for the GAN is to generate fake content that appears as real. In the case of Simulation, I suspect the GAN leverages two inputs: (1) what the Machine is generating as Simulation as the and (2) and a copy of the base reality input stream. In this manner, the generator learns to model synthetic backdrops that the Simulation Function injects into the virtualization layer as backdrop.

Back to how virtualization factors into the computational architecture of the Actual-Social Simulation. An analogy would be a car and a road are both needed for driving. Actual-Universal dictates the car, road, and driving are all simulated. In comparison, Actual-Social simulates driving the car while the road is virtualized backdrop.

Given how virtualization instantiates the Simulation in this context, I do not imagine the Machine filters input or output. This seems true despite working at the Social level of resolution. Like with Actual-Universal, we need all the elements destined for Simulation as input. Be that as it may, it is reasonable to conclude input is limited to just enough of the base reality universe to create a background

---

[16] The terms *real* and *fake* are standard terms in GAN research and not something I created for this book. Real in the context of this book refers to base reality while fake is what the GAN is generating as a synthetic mirror of what the Machine knows about base reality.

for the set of social constructions that give rise to the level of resolution of the Actual Simulation. This is where we can call back to the idea of an aperture I alluded to in the introduction to this level of resolution.

The Social aperture is a selection for the level of base reality input making its way into the Machine Simulation Function. We are not filtering for social elements. Doing so would imply the input consists of nothing but social elements. Instead, the Machine closes the aperture slightly such that less of the base reality universe is present in the input. In turn, more of the social elements are available from the input to the Simulation Function.

§2.2 What?

Since we are still discussing Actual Simulation, what the Machine simulates is the result of a one-to-one mapping between base reality and simulated reality. The Social Simulation would be a de facto mirror of base reality. Said differently, what the Machine simulates in the Social context must be what exists in a social context within base reality. However, we are no longer considering a Universal set as its own subset. Instead, the subset is the set of elements and details related to society and social interaction. We can again describe Simulation in terms of its variance, repetition and change, and fidelity.

The degree of variance within the Actual Simulation at the Social level of resolution would be effectively zero. This is identical to the Universal resolution. However, at the same time, outside of social relations variance could be nonzero. This implies subsequent Actual-Social Simulations would be identical but the backdrop for those Simulations could vary. PKD's *The Man in the High Castle* illustrates this concept. American, German, and Japanese societies show zero variance although the backdrop of the universe is different.

This would be observable from base reality of course and lends credence to a broader idea of Simulation configuration. I don't mean to imply intent. I don't want to introduce the question of *why* either. Rather, I mention observability of variance as a contrast for capacity for variance as two different effects. One exists in the Simulation and the other in the backdrop. Bearing in mind this capacity in the Actual-Social Simulation, we should explore to what extent a Machine might repeat social elements or changes to social constructs in this type of Simulation.

From the view within the Simulation, I don't think elements would repeat or change across time outside of what base reality provided as input. More specifically, there would not be the chance for a *glitch* to occur related to a Programmer modifying the Simulation. Once instantiated, the Machine, Simulation Function, and substrate lock Actual-Social Simulation into its course. The Simulation becomes unalterable, immutable.

We should not consider this odd. Immutability has precedence in computing, especially when the object is critical to the integrity of the system. In your computer, for instance, there are immutable files belonging to the operating system. For the sake of completeness, there are obviously files- created by you- that are fully mutable. Then, there are files that are immutable to you but are mutable to the system itself.

Yet, repetition and change could be possible. If there is any change it would be outside of the Social level of resolution, in the backdrop. Therefore, any noticeable phenomena indicative of a repetition or change to the Simulation would manifest in that context. My thought is this change would not be observable from within the Simulation. Indirectly however, I wonder if there might be some effect on the fidelity of the Actual-Social Simulation.

Granted, the Social level of resolution is different from the Universal despite existing as a subset of the base reality universe. However, to be operationally convincing and functional, the Social must be indistinguishable from base reality social constructs.

Consequently, at one layer of analysis there is little room for difference between levels of resolution across the Actual Simulation type. This is true because of the strength or tightness of the coupling associated with one-to-one mapping. In the end, at least a portion of the computational architecture is identical. At the same time, considering we have discussed the introduction of a hypervisor and an input filter, the Social resolution might have something different for us to consider. Indeed, as much as we are working in the centered social aperture, we also have a universal background. Here, the background ought to have proportionately less fidelity simply because of it not being a focal point for the Simulation.

For one thing, we must discriminate between the Social resolution and the backdrop resolution. Certainly, the Social resolution must be the same as the equivalent structures from base reality. We are still in an Actual Simulation type. Concurrently, the backdrop may deviate from the base reality analogues. Additionally, the increase in count of components undergirding the Actual-Social Simulation brings about a direct rise in complexity. Fortunately, we can look to error rates or degrees of accuracy as first measures for fidelity in this context.

The possibility for error or reduced accuracy is the first crack in the Actual Simulation façade. While I don't believe the error rate could sufficiently be high as to be noticeable, it very well could be nonzero because of the computational processing pipeline of input, to filter, to Machine Simulation Function, to hypervisor. Suffice it to say, that is enough complexity to warrant the most ECC as the Machine could manage while accepting that some errors may slip through.

Any such errors slipping through the ECC mechanisms ought to visible to the Programmer vis-à-vis precision-measuring instrumentation. Given that we are admitting a level of error, a loss in accuracy, it is reasonable to conclude that the precision is less than perfect. I would point out, however, that precision less than zero does not imply the errors exceed a normal tolerance. Further, and this is more likely I think, the precision within the Social Simulation is precise enough to not negatively affect perception or experience. The Machine and Simulation Function confine errors to the backdrop.

Another way to express this idea would be to say that Actual-Social Simulation has two fidelity measures of sensitivity: one for inside the Simulation and another for the backdrop. Likewise, the Machine expresses the overarching Simulation according to two different capabilities. The inner sensitivity and capability must be such that there is no deviation from base reality, no variance from what constitutes social interaction.

At the same time, the sensitivity and capability need not be so stringent outside of social interaction. Input-output patterns, stimuli feedback, and feedforward functions are enough to drive the Simulation because we are in the Actual type. Nonetheless, there is room for fidelity to be different if not demonstrably less than what we understand about Actual-Universal Simulation. In turn, this makes me wonder about the implementation of time in Actual-Social.

§2.3 When?

I suspect time at the Social level of resolution behaves identically to the Universal level of resolution. Regardless of which *how* answer is true, time is still necessarily mapped tick for tock between base reality and the Simulation. The accuracy of this seems to be rooted in the fact we are still in an Actual, as opposed to Virtual or Mental, operational construct.

With that being said, I do see how the Machine would need to pin time. The pinning corresponds to the *inside* the Social Simulation and, separately, *outside* of it in the backdrop. Further, by pinning the time at instantiation the clocks in their respective places ought to keep synchronization with each other and with base reality even though the clocks stand for different base reality timelines.

Pinning is not a foreign concept in computing. For instance, a computer can force processes- that is, running programs- to execute on specific components. A common use of pinning is to isolate a process onto a specific CPU core. Doing so ensures the process has dedicated compute power distributed to it and can keep the process from conflicting with other, adjacent processes.

§2.4 Constraints

Despite process isolation though, there are still computational constraints at play. The overarching constraint scheme for the Actual-Social Simulation is the combination of natural law and selected normative social constructs. I don't know the combination is materially different from Actual-Universal, but it is safe to say the constraints are more focused because of the aperture closing down to the Social resolution.

The architecture change affects compute power. Specifically, the hypervisor introduces approximately 10% compute power overhead. In other words, there is only 90% compute power available to the Simulation as the Machine reserves 10% for its own operation. Even in modern 21st century virtualization this overhead is not a factor given the overabundance of compute power compared to compute load demands. Perhaps if this were a Universal level of resolution the overhead might be more impactful.

As well, I don't think the presence of the hypervisor affects energy and storage. The base reality Machine is still supplying hardware support for the Simulation and both energy and storage are physical constraints primarily. Storage might be more efficient within the same constraint factors given a subset of the universe is the basis of the Simulation. In parallel, the backdrop could be a single storage object shared across all Actual-Social Simulations running on the same base reality Machine.

Like energy and storage, signaling and communication constraints between the involved components of Actual-Social Simulation would not be any different. Both would continue to require lossless, jitter-free, and real-time transmission mechanisms. Thus, signaling and communications constraints certainly affect the Simulation as outlined in Actual-Universal because of the integration of the Type 1 hypervisor.

Compared to Actual-Universal, the interoperability of the Social Simulation would remain the same. Only a Machine with a compatible Type 1 hypervisor would be able to instantiate the Simulation. Furthermore, extensibility in the direction of the Simulation would not change because of the overarching type (Actual). Likewise, the base reality Machine would not suddenly become extensible because of how the hypervisor is effectively the Machine in base reality.

Regardless of the operational importance of virtualization to Actual-Social Simulation, a non-corrupt input from base reality is necessary. Further, the input must keep integrity throughout the Simulation Function and hypervisor layers. In this way, integrity checking is not a different constraint implementation. The Machine, Simulation Function, and substrate just implements it in more places along the computational pipeline.

§3 Actual Simulation: Individual Level of Resolution

The most straightforward way I can conceive of this third form of Actual Simulation is to imagine participation in being me, as an individual, is participation in a Simulation. Therefore, the elements and details of the reality I, as an individual, interact with are the Simulation. The Machine also simulates interactions. Yet, as we discussed in the Actual-Social Simulation, the Machine may not be simulating the object of the interaction.

In terms of Set Theory, I think we can agree the individual is a subset of the universe. Fair enough; that leaves us to work out whether the subset holds all individuals (i.e., me and everyone else) or is a single element subsct (i.e., just me). That is the easy part, however.

If I'm being completely transparent here, I struggle to not think of an Actual-Individual Simulation as nested within either the Actual-Universal or Actual-Social. There are clues we can tease out of the Actual-Individual artifacts. Given the mapping of elements between base reality and the Simulation is still one-to-one, we can start again with how the Machine, Simulation Function, and substrate generate the Simulation.

§3.1 How?

By now we have a measure of familiarity and comfort with the essential mechanisms of Simulation. That is, we know base reality supplies input to a Machine. We know a Programmer has set up a Simulation Function which acts on the input and produces output as the Simulation we are discussing. Fair enough. We also know the Machine has an aperture functionality with which it can narrow the input stream.

Nevertheless, you might have predicted there is a slight twist for us to explore as we discuss how an Actual Simulation at the Individual level of resolution works. Certainly, substrate and fidelity continue as artifacts of the Simulation are at the heart of this work.

Following the logic established so far, it should be clear that the Actual Simulation type bounds the implementation of any level of resolution. Additionally, the level of resolution decides the elements and constructs mapped between base reality and the type of Simulation. If that is true, we can position the substrate as the medium through which all of implementation and mapping occurs.

Undoubtedly, the substrate in the Individual level of resolution supports the one-to-one relation discussed in the Universal and Social resolutions. Moreover, the Simulation is occurring at the level of individual consciousness. I suggest this level of resolution is the most tightly coupled to its substrate.

At the same time, the nature of the one-to-one relation leads us to one twisting departure from the Universal and Social resolutions. The commonality of substrate across instantiations of the Simulation is this departure. Actual Simulation is still one substrate for one Simulation though. Therefore, each Simulation yet exists in a one-dimensional geometry with the base reality individual mapped onto itself.

Yet, the Individual level of resolution needs a common substrate for an infinite set of *me* from base reality. Thus, although the substrate is technically a one-to-one relation, there is an undercurrent of a many-to-many relation because of the multitude of *me* in base reality. I suppose the determination of which of the many to select as a single element for the instantiated relation is based on *when* the Simulation targets which we will discuss forthwith. Regardless, we need to examine virtualization at this level if we are to get the full picture of how the Individual resolution manifests for the Actual Simulation type.

As with Actual-Social Simulation, there are two essential virtualization subcomponents in the Individual level of resolution. One subcomponent is that which instantiates everything of the individual. The other, as you might suspect, is the backdrop or everything not the individual. Bearing that in mind, we have a critical issue to deal with given the separation of these subcomponents.

The issue is which individual does the Machine simulate-the singular individual, a select collection of individuals, or the set of all individuals? If we call back to the overarching Set Theory construct governing the Actual Simulation type, the obvious answer is a singular individual because of one-to-one mapping. However, I suspect the obvious answer is wrong. The *one* in the mapping is the base reality concept of individual to the simulated concept of individual, yes. Yet, the manifestation of the concept is across all individuals (base reality and simulated). Again, the applied Set Theory makes this necessarily so and computation must follow from it.

We then need to decide *how* the collective individual from base reality becomes instantiated in the Simulation. My take is that I don't think the Individual Simulation is loaded into a pre-existing Simulation. Instead, what seems likely to me, is the Machine injects the Individual Simulation into the backdrop. I realize how closely this feels like *nesting,* but I don't think injection and nesting are the same computational actions. To better understand how the two are different, let's consider the manner of execution for each.

With injection, the substrate must load the Simulation backdrop first. Thus, if the backdrop does not load or has a runtime issue the injection cannot occur. Furthermore, the Machine couples the injection to the backdrop. The Machine uses the same coupling mechanism with the hardware substrate. Overall, this injection has a hard dependency on the Machine. This is precisely how services load on modern computers and how computers load programs into memory.

Conversely, nesting implies a computational object is instantiated into the same type of parent object. In this way, a Type 1 hypervisor nests within a Type 1 virtualized foundation. Or, in other words, a physical Machine nested within another physical Machine. While nesting is valid computational feature- running a program within another program is trivial - trying to nest a physical substrate in a physical foundation is clearly implausible. For completeness, Type 1.5 and Type 2 hypervisors are *programs.*

All that said, I am continuing with the car analogy I presented in the Actual-Social virtualization section. Previously, I suggested driving was equivalent to Social Simulation. With Actual-Individual Simulation, the Simulation is the individual experiencing the act or behavior of driving. While subtle, the difference is one layer deeper based on experiencing versus driving. Furthermore, I want to point out the Actual-Individual type implies the Machine (or substrate more appropriately) simulates all individuals experiencing the act of Simulation.

I suppose a natural follow-up question is whether Actual-Individual Simulation could simulate a singular individual. That's a great and fair question. The straightforward answer is *no*. The rationale for the answer rests in how narrow the aperture can close combined with how input or output filtering would not be possible.

Without a doubt, the input aperture is progressively narrower at the Individual level of resolution compared to Social. In this way, I understand the motivation to think the aperture would be capable of narrowing to the singular individual degree. However, I think the salient point in the rationale is that an Actual backdrop is necessary. Too narrow of an aperture would exclude necessary, one-to-one mapped elements related to everything not the singular individual.

Lastly, I can imagine how the Machine and substrate might implement an input or output filter. The filter would by proxy select a singular individual amongst all individuals. Yet again we confront the reality forced upon the Simulation by Set Theory. In other words, because base reality holds the collective Individual, so too must the Actual Simulation. Otherwise, we would be dealing with a different kind of subset and therefore a different form of Simulation.

§3.2 What?

An interesting consequence of the Individual level of resolution is the *me* the Machine simulates is a rendering of *me* in base reality. Further, the Machine manifests *you* and *everyone* likewise. Computationally, this reflects how Actual Simulation works as a relation between the base reality set and itself. Further, with the simulated individual as the operational subset, variance, repetition, and change, as well as fidelity are most certainly going to manifest different than the earlier two levels of resolution.

Observably, the variance between a base reality individual and the corresponding simulated individual ought to be as near zero as the Actual-Universal or Actual-Social instances. An effect of the Individual level of resolution however would be the view from base reality would seem like peering into a mirror. The reflection metaphor is apt here given the one-to-one relation and physical substrate using what is fundamentally a pass-through Simulation Function.

This is how reflective surfaces or reflections appear in throughout the source material. Objects such as mirrored sunglasses, mirrors, and windows are at once portals into Simulations as well as reflective relations of base reality onto itself. While the writers of *The Matrix* films or even Plato may not have deliberately created reflections as symbolic of the computational one-to-one relation, I don't believe we are stretching too far with this interpretation.

Notably, because of how the Actual-Individual Simulation is instantiated, the observation from base reality could be situated in a different time than the reflected individual in the Simulation. More on this when we discuss time.

The last point I want to make related to variance is to recognize that variation may exist between different individuals in the same Simulation. Such a point might be obvious; I get it. Yet, I want to make it explicit to acknowledge what variance can exist between iterations of the same individual across instantiations if the input is not identical across those iterations.

In line with Actual-Universal and Actual-Social, I am doubtful of Actual-Individual Simulation manifesting repetition or change within the Simulation to a degree that is perceptible. Likewise, even though the backdrop holds more material (the universe and social fabrics), I just don't see a way the Simulation could intentionally or unintentionally manifest a glitch. There seems to be no escaping the immutability of the Actual Simulation type as far as I can reason it.

There was a moment when I considered if it might be possible for the Simulation Function to introduce a *glitch* into the input stream. However, logically this would not be a glitch in the way we are using the term. Because the insertion would take place in base reality, the individual would not experience a state transition, a before and after. Similarly, I thought about a scenario whereby the Machine restarts. Ultimately, because of how an Actual Simulation is instantiated across all three levels of resolution, either the identical Simulation would be reloaded where it left off or what is loaded is a different Simulation.

Fidelity, across its five dimensions, measures how well the Simulation appears as real. Because of this fact the Actual-Individual Simulation demands a fidelity equal with an individual participating in a convincing, Actual reality. As much as fidelity is the same in this case as in prior cases, it is also different of course. The difference is first noticeable in the resolution.

Resolution, as we first discussed as a part of Actual-Universal Simulation, exists as a measure of how well the Machine renders mapped elements from base reality into the Simulation. Think about a TV; it both receives and renders. Implicitly, there is a mapping function present. The output must not only faithfully stand for the received input but also render according to a specified resolution. For this artifact, there is a Simulation Function performing the same manner of computation as the TV with a resolution of the individual and its interactions with itself, others, and the universe. Concurrently, unlike the TV but like Actual-Social, the Simulation also has a backdrop with a dissimilar resolution.

The difference at the Individual level of resolution then is the increased computational overhead associated with managing both an extended backdrop and the focal point of the individual. The backdrop holds both the universe and society. Concurrently, the focal point of the individual moves from the diffused resolution (e.g., 480p in a TV) to a focused resolution (e.g., 4k in a TV). Bit for bit, pixel for pixel, the more focused resolution needs an upscaling in computational undergirding.

The increased computational demand related to resolution has side effects when considering error rates and accuracy in the Simulation. Inasmuch as the Actual-Social showed nonzero but imperceptible error rates, the Actual-Individual potentially has an error rate that is sufficiently nonzero to be perceptible under certain conditions. I strongly suspect those conditions revolve around modulation of the Simulation accuracy wherein the modulation is in shifting elements between backdrop and Individual level of resolution.

While I doubt the Programmer shifts elements between backdrop and Simulation, the Programmer would be able to see errors. The Programmer could observe a reduction in precision through the backdrop as elements shift into the Individual level of resolution. The evidence would emerge from interactions within the upscaled resolution framing.

It follows then that the Actual-Individual Simulation would add an added sensitivity measure of fidelity in the barrier between the backdrop and Simulation. There would still be independent sensitivity measures in those two components as well. Further, I suggest the sensitivity measure for the Individual Simulation is commensurately more advanced much in the same way and for the same reasons as the resolution aspect is upscaled in this artifact. Thus, the Machine and substrate support the fidelity of the overarching Actual Simulation. We are still well within the realm of one-to-one mapping then. However, the capability of the underlying architecture might at its limits.

§3.3 When?

Next to *how* and *what*, an Actual Simulation at the Individual level of resolution would computationally have two *when's* to track. One timeline would correspond to an overarching continuum consistent with the relation between base reality time and simulated time. Then, framed by the individual relation to Simulation, a potentially second time would be part of the feeling of the individual. As a result, pinning individual clocks becomes even more important for the supporting of consistent tick rates.

We should be careful to disambiguate the two forms of time here. I am not suggesting the Simulation contains the nested individual's feeling of time. Rather, the perceived time is adjacent or to use Philip K. Dick's term *lateral*. Moreover, while the Machine would synchronize the underlying tick or rhythm, not only could the origin time be different as we discussed in Actual-Universal and Actual-Social, but the inner Simulation time as perceived by the individual could drift, could drag or rush in tempo.

The disconnection between the dual time artifacts stands for a stark shift from the *when* in earlier Simulation types. Yet, I suspect the deviation is natural. More concretely, I think the disconnect is a byproduct of how the Machine loads the Simulation. I strongly suspect the Machine uses *when* to differentiate one Actual-Individual Simulation from all other possible Actual-Individual Simulations. A notable example not discussed in the source material section but still pertinent is Westworld[17].

§3.4 Constraints

The overarching set of constraints for the Actual-Individual Simulation are a convergence of base reality natural law and the perspective of the simulated individual interacting with itself. An unavoidable constraint on the Individual level of resolution stems from the mechanisms necessary within the Simulation Function. Specifically, the Simulation Function constrains the aperture closing to *anything* not an individual. Logically, the aperture problem is closely related to the potential loss of accuracy and precision associated with the shifting of elements between backdrop and Simulation as part of *what* the Machine simulates. For that reason, I believe it is safe to assume the constraints are designed with a particular focus on the aperture.

Keeping the Simulation aperture closed to anything not the Individual would need dedicated compute power, energy, and even perhaps storage. At the same time, these constraints might apply differently to the backdrop one on hand and the Individual level of resolution on the other. For instance, in general the available base reality universe constrains the Simulation. Therefore, the available compute power and energy remain finite as has been the case throughout the Actual Simulation type.

In the case of storage, I imagine the Machine leverages partitioning. Partitioning is a method to create separate logical spaces atop a physical substrate. The operating system- the Simulation in this case- treats each partition

---

[17] Both the *Westworld* movie and HBO show demonstrate this concept of *when* in terms of a simulated (Individual) reality. Regarding the HBO show, I find it interesting how Simulation themes overlap between it and *The Matrix* films. Both have sentient artificial intelligence; both have computational underpinnings expressed symbolically in narrative form. As well, *Westworld* and *The Matrix* focus on a simulated reality reflected in an Actual but time-disconnected manner.

as separate, distinct storage. This means the Machine can apply different *rules* to the various partitions without affecting the each equally. If this is true, there might be a set of rules for backdrop storage and a different ruleset for the Individual Simulation. In turn, by using rules for access control, read or write prioritization, compression, and so forth, the Machine and Simulation Function can computationally affect the aperture.

Likewise, because the narrowness of the aperture is critical, all signaling and communication between Simulation components needs to be efficient and resilient. More than Actual-Universal and Actual-Social, the throughput of signaling and communication is of higher importance than the quality. This might seem counterintuitive. However, I suspect the fidelity of the Individual Simulation is such that too little throughput would have a more negative impact than loss, jitter, and so forth.

With that in mind, I feel efficiency is at once a constraint and an effect. The effect is related to the lack of input-output filtering in the Actual Simulation type. As a constraint, ensuring signaling and communication occur only when necessary and carry only the element information needed reduces the likelihood of forcing the aperture open past the Actual-Individual artifact.

In conjunction with efficiency, signaling and communication needs to be resilient. In view of the increased potential for errors in what is being Simulation, the Actual-Individual substrate could have a sense of signal state (e.g., sent, received, waiting). Then, based on intended state, the Simulation Function could respond with a compensating function. For example, if the signal approaches an accuracy and precision threshold based on errors, the Machine could stop and restart the signal. This would prevent the error rate from producing obvious glitches in the Simulation.

Notwithstanding the changes in prior constraints, it strikes me as rationale for interoperability to remain restricted to identical base reality Machine architectures. The coupling of the Simulation to its physical substrate is just too strong to allow interoperability. Similarly, once instantiated, there would not be an opportunity to extend the Actual-Individual Simulation. Be that as it may, I can foresee how Individual interactions with the Simulation could externally be observable as tantamount to extensibility. At least in the Actual-Individual Simulation, this is illusion.

As well, more so than other constraints, I think the physical and logical architecture differences associated with Actual-Individual Simulation influence integrity checking. Moreover, I suspect the influence seen here will have far-reaching effects in later Simulation types and levels of resolution.

There are two reasons for my assertion. Principally, integrity checking can be computationally expensive if the object is either large or there are many objects to be checked concurrently. This is inescapable due to the mathematics involved. What is more, the complexity of the integrity checking implementation inevitably rises as the complexity of the Simulation architecture expands. Put simply, there necessarily is more integrity checking taking place.

Before moving on, I want to mention a loss of integrity does not imply there is something wrong. While the computational Simulation object could indeed lose integrity by not existing in an intended state, I think it will be more likely that the Simulation Function, substrate, and hypervisor-virtualization layers will not be able to keep up. Consequently, I wonder to what extent we might encounter divergence, glitches, and material oddities in the Virtual and Mental types of Simulation.

Dr. Scalambrino

Philosophically speaking, all levels of resolution regarding an "actual" type of Simulation, in Simulation theory, refer to the idea that our entire experience of reality is *actually* the experience of a Simulation. As noted in the Introduction, Plato's writings provide a valuable means toward conceptualizing Actual Simulation. Also, the Buddhist understanding of sensory experience, and the film *12 Monkeys* may be helpful for understanding Actual Simulation.

A key aspect to Actual Simulation is the idea that "base reality" is inaccessible. That's why *The Matrix* may not be the best example to invoke when explaining Actual Simulation. Rather, films involving "time travel" may function better in that, in such films, when a protagonist occupies another time, the protagonist no longer has experiential access to the time from which they came.

In an Actual Simulation, base reality is inaccessible to experience. We can think it. For example, if we are in an Actual Simulation, then we can write a book about it, but we can't gain experiential knowledge of the reality out of which the Simulation we occupy is being generated. Philosophically, this is characterized as the difference between an object of experience and a thing-in-itself. It is useful to hyphenate the term "thing-in-itself" to indicate that its true nature is beyond experience.

Further, it is useful to keep in mind the distinction between *thinking about* base reality and *experiencing* base reality. The idea here is that in the actual type of Simulation, whatever kind of reality base reality may be, what makes the type of Simulation actual is that we cannot experience base reality. In *The Matrix* films, protagonists are able to exit the Matrix and experience the reality out of which the machines are generating the Matrix, that is, the Simulation. Thus, *The Matrix* films are best invoked as an example for other types of Simulation (virtual and mental).

§4 Actual Simulation: Universal Level of Resolution

To say that we are in an Actual Simulation is to say that the reality we experience is, somehow, being generated and that the "reality" in which we dwell and have our experiences is not base reality. The two concepts that immediately come to mind here should be the Buddhist understanding of the "skandas" or "Five Aggregates" and Plato's Cave. In the language of the continental philosophical tradition, then, we would say that as we experience the cosmos, the *things* of the cosmos *in-themselves* are converted into the objects we experience. And, thus, we don't experience things as they are in base reality.

Further, to think about Actual Simulation at the universal level of resolution is to understand that all of us, that is, the entire human race – perhaps it may be better to say "all sentient beings" – participate in the Actual Simulation. In other words, when we think of Actual Simulation at the universal level of resolution, there is no experience possible that does not happen within the Simulation. This will, of course, be understood differently at the social and individual levels of resolution.

The value of the essential distinction, noted above, regarding accessibility, can be seen here. If we are in an Actual Simulation, then whatever may be functioning as a hypervisor, whatever may be generating the Simulation is concealed from us. So, whether we think along the lines of the Five Aggregates in Buddhism or embodiment in the third dimension in Plato's Cave, experience is understood as contained, constrained, or conditioned by, the Simulation. In other words, in an Actual Simulation all of experience takes place within the Simulation, and there is no experience of base reality. Importantly, in an actual type of Simulation, base reality is not ambiguous, it is inaccessible. Thus, the exact same examples may be invoked across all types of Simulation, but what makes the examples essentially different is that in an Actual Simulation there is no experiential access to base reality.

§4.1 How?

To ask, then, "How" an Actual Simulation is possible, philosophically, is to focus on the difference between the levels of "reality" distinguished by their accessibility to experience. In other words, if the third dimension is a Simulation of a higher dimension, then in the higher – base reality – dimension, there may not be an equivalent to experience. Think of it like this: If experience requires sensation and sensation requires physical embodiment, then if an essential difference between the higher and lower dimensions is that we are not physically embodied in the higher dimension, then there could be no "experience" of that higher – base reality – dimension. As we will see, Simulation is understood quite differently in the virtual and mental types. Thus, philosophically, when we ask the "How" question regarding Actual Simulation, we find a different set of possible answers from the sets found in the other types. First and foremost, in an Actual Simulation, none of us are responsible for generating the Simulation.

Thus, when we ask "How" regarding Actual Simulation, concepts regarding God, gods, karma, and intelligent design seem most relevant for explaining the generation of the Simulation. Bostrom's notion of an advanced civilization only makes sense, here, if we understand our experience of reality as completely separate from the civilization occupying the base reality out of which the reality we experience is being generated. In other words, regarding this type of Simulation at this level of resolution it is not enough to recognize that are incapable of experiencing base reality; rather, we must also recognize that we should not "anthropomorphize" base reality.

Perhaps, as in the film *12 Monkeys*, there is some way for participants in the Simulation to communicate with the civilization in base reality; however, in order for a Simulation to be the actual type at the universal level of resolution, the assumption that the "civilization" generating the Simulation is the same as our civilization would entail having impossible knowledge, since we cannot experience outside of the Simulation. At the same time, it would, rather, seem to logically follow that the reality of whatever "civilization" is generating the Simulation we consider reality is quite different from the reality we experience.[18]

§4.2 When?

Recall, from the Introduction, above, when discussing the difference between time in base reality and time in a Simulation: the two times may be different; they may be the same; or, we may not be able to discern their relation. In order, then, to answer the question "When?" regarding an Actual Simulation, that is, the question of how the experience of time relates to time in base reality, the following contrast may be helpful. Consider the difference between the films *12 Monkeys* (1995), *The Matrix* (1999), and *Inception* (2010).

In *12 Monkeys* the protagonist, played by Bruce Willis, is sent into the past to determine "what went wrong." Now, insofar as Bruce Willis was an actual inhabitant of the future civilization (a prisoner) whom they sent into the past, his capacities for experiencing reality were the same as those of the other members of the future civilization. Yet, at the same time, insofar as he can be "pulled back" from the past and insofar as he can change the past, then the period of space and time into which he was sent may be understood as a Simulation.

---

[18] In fact, this would follow from the logic of Bostrom's own justification. Recall, according to Bostrom, an advanced civilization may have created the Simulation we experience as reality to work out potential futures, not merely for their entertainment, as if we are *The Sims* in their computers. So long as a civilization would create a Simulation not merely for entertainment purposes, then the Simulation should be the testing of various hypotheses, the outcome of which may give the civilization insight with which to make their own future choices in base reality. However, notice, all of that assumes base reality even takes place in time as we experience it and that our experiences would somehow be structurally similar enough to the members of the base reality civilization to provide them with valuable insight regarding their own (base) reality. Yet, given the very nature of Actual Simulation at the universal level of resolution, such assumptions should be understood as constituting misunderstandings.

Notice, there is a clear contrast with *The Matrix*, in which Morpheus, played by Laurence Fishburne, tells Neo, played by Keanu Reeves, that they no longer know the time of base reality. Inside the Simulation that is the Matrix, the people experience time passing and have a definite understanding of "where" they are, so to speak, in history, that is, the history of their reality. However, because the Matrix is being generated out of a base reality with a different history, the timelines of the Simulation and base reality seem to run parallel, even though the time of base reality is unknown, the time of the Matrix is computer generated. In other words, being "re-inserted" back into the Matrix isn't time traveling. It isn't going backward or forward in time; rather, time is passing in base reality, and the passage of time is being simulated in the Matrix.

Lastly, invoking *Inception* here may be helpful. The protagonist in *Inception*, played by Leonardo DiCaprio, enters into a dream. The structure of that entering into a dream is very much like the structure of entering into the Matrix, with three important differences. First, the biggest difference is that – because a dream can be entered from within a dream – the film may be understood as remaining ambiguous regarding base reality. That is to say, it may be the case that the protagonist was always already in a dream, and the audience never actually witnesses what would be base reality in *Inception*. Thus, second, it is not possible to discern the temporal relation between being in a dream, as Simulation, and being in base reality. Thus, third, unless the ambiguity is resolved in some way, it is not possible to know if the protagonist is "traveling in time" by entering into a Simulation (that is, a dream).

Contrasting these three films, then, is helpful for thinking through the question of how the experience of time in an Actual Simulation relates to time in base reality. Simply put, there are three temporal relations a Simulation may have to base reality. The two times may be different; they may be the same; or, we may not be able to discern their relation. Because it is an essential feature of an Actual Simulation that protagonists cannot have an experience of base reality, it is consistent with the logic of Simulation theory to say that the relation between time in an actual type of Simulation and base reality is unknowable. Again, this is not because the temporal relation is ambiguous, but, rather, it is because we cannot know what *the experience* of time in base reality is like.

§4.3 Constraints

Recall, ontologically, base reality in an Actual Simulation is inaccessible and unknowable. When we take the position that we are in some type of Simulation, then, it is easy to recognize the relation between simulated reality and base reality may be characterized in terms of constraints. The constraints that immediately come to mind are constraints regarding experience, understanding, and causality/reciprocal influence. In his essay "Schizophrenia and the Book of Changes," written in 1965, Philip K. Dick had the following to say about time and causality.

> What distinguishes schizophrenic existence from that which the rest of us like to image we enjoy is the element of time. The schizophrenic is having it all now, whether he wants it or not; the whole can of film has descended on him, whereas we watch it progress frame by frame. So, for him, causality does not exist. Instead, the a-causal connective principle ... called Synchronicity is operating in all situations – not merely as one factor at work, as with us. Like a person under LSD, the schizophrenic is engulfed in an endless now. (Dick, 1995: xvi).

Though I disagree with Dick's characterization of psychosis, thinking through this passage may be fruitful for understanding the relation between time in an Actual Simulation and time in base reality.

On the one hand, we could consider either the schizophrenic experience of time or the non-schizophrenic experience of time as base reality. More importantly though, is this idea of an "endless now." The reason this is important is because it is an idea that has always been present in the history of Western philosophy. Whether it was called the "*hic et nunc*" or the "standing now," this is not a new idea, and it is not an idea derived from LSD or schizophrenia. On the other hand, there are multiple ways to understand an "endless now."

If we say that the past is not real, because it is "gone," and the future is not real, because it is not "here yet," then, suddenly, we can recognize that the now is all that is ever real. This is one understanding of an endless now, and, certainly, that true, LSD or not. Yet, it is also possible to understand base reality as a kind of eternal Becoming – Aristotle likens it in his *Metaphysics* to "motion in a circle" – such that base reality is an eternality which can only be experienced as an endless now. It could also be the case that base reality is a higher dimension in which it would be more appropriate to speak of a sphere than a circle; and, were that the case, then the linear movement implied by tracing the circumference of a circle could no longer be assumed.

Though this discussion will be helpful throughout the rest of the book, in regard to the actual type of Simulation, we again stop at the impasse which is an essential feature distinguishing the actual type of Simulation from other types of Simulation, namely, we cannot know how the experience of time in an Actual Simulation relates to time in base reality. In an Actual Simulation, we cannot know how our being in the time of the Simulation relates to the being in time of base reality.

§4.4 Transcendence

Just as it is clear that inhabiting a Simulation may constrain one's experience of base reality, so too there may be ways for inhabits to "transcend" simulated reality toward base reality. In contrast to the virtual and mental types of Simulation, it is an essential and defining feature of the actual type of Simulation that inhabitants of an

Actual Simulation cannot *experience* base reality. Thus, mystical experiences and even the experience of being "abducted by aliens" may not reveal the reality of base reality. Rather, it may be the case that all of our encounters with base reality manifest within the constraints of what the Simulation can contain. This is, precisely, the philosophical distinction between the object of experience and the thing-in-itself again.

Thus, we cannot understand transcendence in regard to the Actual Simulation type as "leaving" the Simulation for base reality. Perhaps (and this is the biggest kind of perhaps there is), death may be the path to transcending the Simulation, but even if death is the path to "leaving" the Simulation, there may be actions which need to take place within the Simulation, if one is to leave the Simulation and "arrive" in base reality. However, despite the universality of the constraints regarding Actual Simulation (at the universal level of resolution), a kind of transcendence may still be possible.

If thinking through being in an Actual Simulation changes one's relation to the experiences had in the Simulation, then that change may constitute a kind of transcendence. Of course, the question would be: Are we transcending, or are we sinking deeper into, the Simulation? Thus, the defining feature of transcendence for an Actual Simulation may simply be gaining control of one's actions within simulated reality by way of having gained some insight into one's simulated state of being. Transcendence will look different in the other types of Simulation, but for the actual type at the universal level, this may be the only kind of transcendence which is within our own power to accomplish.

Finally, in terms of artifacts of the Simulation – signs or clues to indicate that one might be living in a Simulation – regarding Actual Simulation at the universal level of resolution, synchronicity seems to be the artifact regarding which there is the most agreement. That is to say, it seems that many thinkers regarding Simulation theory consider *the experience* of synchronicity to point to something that transcends the Actual Simulation, some thing-in-itself in base reality. Whether this is a communication from base reality or not, will, for the actual type of Simulation at the universal level of resolution, remain cloaked in ambiguity and ineffability.

§5 Actual Simulation: Social Level of Resolution

There is actually a significant difference between the social and universal levels of resolution, regarding the actual type of Simulation in Simulation theory. What the social level of resolution means here is that an Actual Simulation is generated at the social level. Thus, an Actual Simulation at the social level of resolution refers to a group of individuals participating in a Simulation, and the rest of the non-social group either in base reality or participating in a different type of Simulation.

If the individuals outside the social Simulation are participating in a Simulation, then the actual social-level Simulation is a nested Simulation. If the individuals outside the social Simulation are in base reality, then the socialization is itself the Simulation. The essential distinction here refers, again, to actuality. In other words, it may be easier to see the actual genera and social species of Simulation in contrast to Virtual Simulation. Thus, in the virtual genera of Simulation, the social species refers to a social way of being that is simulated, though participants in that Simulation can still be social without being in a Simulation. In other words, it is a subset of socialization that is a Virtual Simulation; rather than, with Actual Simulation at the social level, socialization is itself the Simulation.

§5.1 How?

To ask, then, "How" an actual social Simulation is possible, philosophically, is to focus on the relation between the social and non-social. Hence, with the actual type of Simulation at the social level of resolution, we have the idea that structures in society are placeholders, like realities in a game, and playing the various roles associated with the social realities is participating in a Simulation. Consider how this relates to Plato's Cave. With Actual Simulation at the universal level of resolution, we considered how all of reality was a Simulation. As Plato's *Republic* continues, the dialogue where we find the Myth of the Cave (in Book VII), Plato went on to discuss types of government. This is where the social level of Actual Simulation is taking place. Each *form* of government may be understood as a type of Simulation insofar as the form is Platonically understood as more real than the protagonists who people it. Thus, we can say that the protagonists participate in an actual social Simulation because the form of government determines their experience of base reality.

The question remains, what are the individuals outside the social group experiencing? Are they experiencing base reality or a Simulation that, though different from the societal Simulation experienced by others, is still a Simulation? If this latter possibility were the case, then it may make most sense to understand the Simulation of the "outsiders" to be a Simulation still (indirectly) determined by the form that determines the social Simulation. For those outside of a Democracy, it is reality that they cannot vote. Yet, were they living in relation to a different form of government, the question of voting may not be essential for them. Hence, the form governing the actual social Simulation may indirectly govern the Simulation in which it is nested.

Of course, if somehow the wilderness of an existence un-exposed to domestication were considered base reality – Rousseau's notion of the Noble Savage comes to mind –, then we might still think of the existential constraints of such a situation to constitute participation in a Simulation. For example, to be dropped into an environment in which one must survive is to participate in the constraints of the terrain and vegetation, and so on. Hence, in regard to the "How?" of an Actual Simulation at the social level of resolution, the following three possibilities seem to sufficiently characterize the logic of Simulation theory at that level of resolution.

One, the social group participates in a Simulation, and the non-, or anti-, social group does not. Two, the social group participates in a Simulation, and the non-social group participates in an Actual Simulation indirectly determined by the form of the social Simulation. Three, the social group participates in a Simulation, and the non-social group participates in a Simulation determined by an ineffable base reality, cloaked in ambiguity, and inaccessible to experience.

§5.2 When?

The question "When?" regarding an Actual Simulation may be easier to envision at the social level of resolution than at the universal level. The idea here should be fairly straightforward. We need only consider forms of government or forms of social participation to be historical in nature. Thus, just as the return to monarchy may be thought of as a return to the past, so too we could speak of future forms of social participation. Here is where Marxist thought first finds its traction. Though Marxist philosophy will appear and be discussed most relevantly in the next chapter regarding the virtual type of Simulation, here we can draw a structural analogy.

According to Marxist thought, though again we'll discuss this more thoroughly below, social reality is conditioned by modes of production and technological advancement. In this way, modes of production and technological advancement constitute the manner in which base reality is transformed into a social Simulation. This is the case because certain forms of social participation are contingent upon the advancement of technology and modes of production. For example, once it becomes possible to automate certain tasks, then one's relation to their environment necessarily changes. All of this fits hand-in-glove with Marxist thought, especially insofar as Marxists speak of the "social construction of reality," they may as well be saying "the construction of a Simulation from out of the present state of technological advancement and modes of production."

Finally, then, in regard to the "When?" question, we can see the logic of Simulation theory emerge, here, regarding actual social Simulation. For, it may be the case that the social Simulation in which one participates is materially-determined by access to technology and the modes of production available to their society. And, in such a case, the social Simulation is a construction relative to a people's means to relate to their environment, which may or may not be considered base reality. Either way, what the "relative to" piece accomplishes here is that it, again, creates a kind of timeline.

Thus, participating in a "past" type of actual social Simulation becomes possible. Yet, we should keep in mind, because this is Actual Simulation, whatever form we participate in, every form refers to a Simulation. The "When" question, then, regarding Actual Simulation at the social level of resolution would really be asking in regard to the "cutting edge" of technological advancement and modes of production. As was argued extensively throughout *Social Epistemology and Technology: Toward Public Self-Awareness Regarding Technological Mediation* (2015), using technology changes one's experience of reality and the manner in which one inhabits their environment. Hence, it becomes possible to speak of living a past form of existence by changing one's relation to the technology mediating experience. Yet, per the actual type of Simulation at the social level of resolution, we need to keep in mind that each of forms available to one by changing one's relation to technology is, ultimately, the form of a social construction.

§5.3 Constraints

Again, the constraints regarding the actual type of Simulation at the social level of resolution are quite similar to the constraints at the universal level of resolution. That is to say, with the actual type of Simulation, we continually find ourselves up against the ambiguity and ineffability concealing base reality. On the one hand, we are constrained from knowing base reality, that is, reality as it is in-itself. On the other hand, we may also be constrained when it comes to the ability to control the advancement of modes of production and technology mediating our experience of reality. For, even to be able to return to a "past" form of social Simulation would take place within a diversely landscaped Actual Simulation. Smartphones and jet planes alongside tribal village life.

§5.4 Transcendence

At the social level of resolution of an Actual Simulation, it is easier to see transcendence than at the universal level of resolution. For, to see that one is more than the role one plays in a social setting, to see that one is more than one's identity as determined by society, is already to gain a transcending insight into living in a Simulation. The two questions that immediately surface, however, are again about the relation between base reality and non-social being. In other words, if we think of social reality as a kind of "herd" existence (following Aristotle and Nietzsche), then the question is whether the herd reality that is a kind of Simulation is itself nested in another Simulation or not. Whereas this is essentially ambiguous regarding Actual Simulation, it will not be ambiguous regarding the virtual type.

In fact, in *Die Fröhliche Wissenschaft* (*The Gay Science* or *The Joyful Quest*, in English), §354 of Book 5, Nietzsche can be read as articulating the manner in which an individual could come to participate in a Simulation simply through adopting social frameworks for understanding self-consciousness, which is itself, according to Nietzsche, developed through participating in a Simulation.

> It was only as a social animal that man acquired self-consciousness – which he is still in the process of doing, more and more.

My idea is, as you see, that *consciousness does not really belong to man's individual existence* [emphasis added] but rather to his social or herd nature; that, as follows from this, it has developed subtlety only insofar as this is required by social or herd utility.

Notice, this is a radical way to understand how one's mind is barred from gaining an awareness of itself as participating in a Simulation. It is radical because it suggests that self-reflection is the reflection of a Simulation. So, to "Know Thy Self" is to overlook that the self depends on a Simulation to appear real to itself.

At the same time, just as a kind of existential authenticity contrasts a merely being "carried along" by technological mediation or, in other words, an inauthentic mode of being constituted by social construction, so too can changing one's relation to technological mediation be understood as a kind of transcendence. In this way, transcendence refers to transcending the constructed Simulation of social reality in which one finds oneself. This includes, of course, cultural and countercultural movements as different ways of navigating a simulated society.

The authentic mode of being as transcending an Actual Simulation does not eliminate the Simulation. Rather, it refers to a third position which contrasts with either embracing or rejecting the socially constructed reality. Being authentic refers to taking an awareness of one's being as a point of departure for relating to one's environment. In this way, existential authenticity is more primordial than any (inauthentic) mode of being that takes the Simulation as its point of departure (cf. Scalambrino, 2021). To reject an identity as a social construction in an Actual Simulation is not the accomplishment of transcendence; rather, the accomplishment of transcendence refers to self-actualization through the realization that all identities are social constructions.

§6 Actual Simulation: Individual Level of Resolution

The final level of resolution regarding the actual type of Simulation is the individual. This level of resolution does not refer to the idea that only one person is participating in a Simulation and everyone else is not. The reason this is called "the individual level of resolution" is because it takes the individual (in contrast to a social group or to the universal idea of "everyone") as its point of departure for thinking through Simulation theory. Further, it does not exclude the possibility of multiple persons participating in a Simulation, though it does not consider their aggregate to necessarily be a group with a society for itself or as a society unto itself.

At this point in the chapter, we have already seen the logic that pertains to the actual level of Simulation. Just as the universal and social levels of resolution may be examined regarding their relation to base reality, so too can the individual level of resolution. And, as we will see, the logic of Actual Simulation, specifically the Simulation's relation to base reality, time, constraints, and transcendence follows the same contours of possibility as the other levels of resolution.

§6.1 How?

There are two comments I would like to make before directly addressing the "How?" question. First, were I to provide a label for Actual Simulation at the individual level of resolution, I would call it Hermetic or Hermeticism. Second, Actual Simulation at the individual level of resolution also harmonizes well with Mahayana Buddhism, what Existentialism calls "the joyful quest," and Plato's discussion of re-incarnation at the end of the *Republic*, the Myth of Er.

To ask, then, "How" an Actual Simulation at the individual level is possible is, first and foremost, to ask: "How is it possible that only some individuals are participating in a

Simulation?" Or, its inverse, "How is it possible that some individuals are not participating in a Simulation?"

When we look at the soteriological structure of enlightenment in Mahayana Buddhism, we find a distinction between nirvana and final nirvana. The idea is that making contact with nirvana transforms an individual. On the one hand, it transforms an individual from a non-arhat to an arhat (aka a Boddhisatva). This means that the person's potential number of rebirths/re-incarnations is radically limited. On the other hand, the transformation guarantees that if not at the end of this incarnation, then at the end of one of the very few – possibly one – rebirths the individual has left, they will encounter final nirvana. Whatever we may wish to say about final nirvana, the idea is that it ceases all rebirths; it ceases all re-incarnations.

Recall, at the beginning of this chapter, I noted: When we ask "How" regarding Actual Simulation, concepts regarding God, gods, karma, and intelligent design seem most relevant for explaining the generation of the Simulation. Thus, along the lines that, *but not necessarily* the case that, physical embodiment is a kind of spiritual lowering or imprisonment, then the analogical connection with Simulation theory becomes easy to see. Unenlightened beings would be those protagonists participating in the Simulation without any non-surface awareness of living in a Simulation. Those individuals who gain sufficient insight into participation in a Simulation to enlighten and place light on the manner in which they are participating in a Simulation change their relation to being in a Simulation. In this way, there may be multiple individuals, otherwise unconnected or aggregate, who participate in a Simulation along with enlightened individuals who are somehow exiting the Simulation, like Neo exiting the Matrix.

The strictly ontological answer to the question of "How?" points to the Myth of Er in Book X of Plato's *Republic*. There, Plato discussed the process of (re)incarnation, suggesting that certain aspects of the individual's next incarnation – the individual's next life – will be fated to it. Plato weaves in the story of the Fates allotting aspects to each individual's next incarnation. Insofar as this is understood as constituting the very self of the individual, it becomes possible to conceive of a persona in a Simulation in terms of archetypes allotted to an individual at the time of their incarnation. Thus, it becomes possible to conceive of a person being allotted to a place within a Simulation.

§6.2 When?

The question "When?" regarding an Actual Simulation at the individual level of resolution, then, should primarily be understood as asking where is the individual located in the cycle of re-incarnating into a Simulation (or "back" into the Simulation). There seem to be two other ways to understand the question "When?" regarding the individual level of resolution.

One, if the relation between enlightenment, "making contact with nirvana," is understood as the top of a ladder or set of stairs, then it would become possible to talk about "falling away from" or "getting closer to" the accomplishment of the spiritual quest. If one adopts such a gradated soteriology, then it becomes possible to answer "When" in terms of from which ladder rung an individual is participating in Simulation. Lastly, "When?" could be answered in terms of which incarnation.

A comment here regarding Philip K. Dick's (PKD's) notion of an "endless now" may be helpful. Keeping the soteriology of enlightenment in mind, mentioned in the previous section, it is possible to think of the "place" from which Simulations are generated and individuals are "inserted" into Simulations. If we think of that "place" as a point of origin, then we can inquire into the difference between the experience of time in a Simulation and time in that "place" of origin. It seems most appropriate, that is, consistent with the logic of Simulation theory and a soteriology of enlightenment, to temporally characterize that place of origin as an endless now.

§6.3 Constraints

Yet again, the constraints regarding the actual type of Simulation at the individual level of resolution are quite similar to the constraints at the universal and the social levels of resolution. That is to say, with the actual type of Simulation, we continually find ourselves up against the ambiguity and ineffability concealing base reality. Moreover, another constraint for the individual level, though it could also be applied to the level of tribes and "a people": It is difficult to discern what has been fated and what has not, what is the result of an accomplished destiny, what is fate, and what is merely good chance. On the one hand, we are constrained from knowing base reality, that is, reality as it is in-itself. On the other hand, we may also be constrained when it comes to the ability to control the advancement of modes of production and technology mediating our experience of reality. For, even to be able to return to a "past" form of social Simulation would take place within a diversely landscaped Actual Simulation. Smartphones and jet planes alongside tribal village life.

§6.4 Transcendence

In regard to transcendence, we have already seen how a soteriology of enlightenment provides a natural framework for thinking about transcendence, that is, transcending a Simulation in which one is participating. On the one hand, keeping with the discussion of a generic soteriology of enlightenment, to see that one is more than the role one plays in a social setting, to see that one is more than one's identity as determined by society, is already to gain a transcending insight into living in a Simulation. On the other hand, Nietzsche's characterization of *Amor Fati* as the culmination of a joyful quest seems to perfectly illuminate the structure of the concept of transcendence in an Actual Simulation at the individual level of resolution.

In order to understand *Amor Fati* in Nietzsche, we also need to understand his concept of the Eternal Return. The following explanation, then, of the Eternal Return and Amor Fati is paraphrased from my book What Is Existentialism? Vol. I, pages 87-90. The Eternal Return, aka the Idea of the Eternal Recurrence of the Same, may be best explained as a characterization of Nature and as an existential test. Moreover, it may be helpful to start by looking at Nietzsche's German: "*die ewige Wiederkehr.*" The term "*ewige*" may also be translated as "everlasting," and "*Wiederkehr*" may be seen as composed of two words: "again" and "turn."[19]

What does "the Eternal Return" mean? When asked in isolation like this, I always invoke *The Joyful Quest* §341. The epigram there is titled: "The greatest weight." Nietzsche asks us to suppose some demon or daimon were to say to us:

> This life as you now live it and have lived it, you will have to live once more and innumerable times more; and there will be nothing new in it, but every pain and every joy and every thought and sigh and everything unutterably small or great in your life will have to return to you, all in the same succession and sequence... (Nietzsche, 1974, §341).

If one is simply asked what is the Eternal Return, that epigram tends to be the response.

Importantly, though, Nietzsche concludes the epigram with a question and a potential response to the question: "Would you not throw yourself down and gnash your teeth and curse the demon who spoke thus?" Notice how Nietzsche characterizes an alternative response: "Or have you once experienced a tremendous moment when you would have answered him: 'You are a god and never have I heard anything more divine.'" (Ibid).

---

[19] This should call to mind, for example, Heidegger's discussions of "the twisting free."

It is in this way that the Eternal Return is discussed as a kind of test. Namely, how would you respond to it? The former response is supposed to be a herd response. It makes sense to call it this given the herd understanding of tragedy and suffering. The latter response is supposed to be the response that would come from the highest order of existence. Why? Because the revelation of divine presence is not lost on the child-like innocence of the highest order, and the point of view of the highest order affirms the divinity involved in the situation further insofar as it acknowledges the fatal identity of the revelation. I mean: if this divine revelation is informing you of your fate, then you will not be able to escape it.

Nietzsche concludes the epigram by noting what may be thought of as a mantra of the highest order.

> If this thought gained possession of you, it would change you as you are or perhaps crush you. The question in each and every thing, 'Do you desire this once more and innumerable times more?' would lie upon your actions as the greatest weight. Or how well disposed would you have to become to yourself and to life to crave nothing more fervently than this ultimate eternal confirmation and seal? (Ibid).

In this way, the Eternal Return may be seen as a principle of selection or a kind of "test." Following Deleuze, I also refer to this as the "selective principle of Eternal Recurrence." The idea here is actually quite straightforward: how you respond to the idea of the Eternal Return may be understood as revealing one's degree of enlightenment as soteriological.

Having said all that, we are ready to read the *Amor Fati* passage from Book 4, §276 of *The Joyful Quest*:

> *To the new year* – Still I live, still I think: I must still live, then I must still think... Today everyone allows the speaking out of wishful and heartfelt thinking: so now I also want to say, what I wish for myself today and which

thought first ran across my heart this year, –
which thought shall be my foundation,
certainty, and sweetness for the rest of my
life! I want to learn more and more, to see the
necessary in things as beautiful: – then I will
be one who makes things beautiful. *Amor
Fati*: shall be my love from now on! I do not
want to wage war on what is ugly. I do not
want to accuse, I do not even want to accuse
the accusers. Looking away will be my only
negation. And, all in all and on the whole: I
wish to be only a Yes-sayer! (Nietzsche, 1974:
223).[20]

Notice, the beginning of the passage coincides with an
existential critique of Descartes (I think, therefore I am).
Further, in regard to the end of the passage, this kind of
"transcendent" Yes-saying relates to existence, it relates to
the necessary (fated) aspects of existence. Interestingly,
though this relation is to fate, not destiny, it also has
consequences for destiny.[21]

On the one hand, consider the last epigram prior to *Amor
Fati*: "What is the seal of liberation? – No longer being
ashamed in front of oneself." This can be understood as
describing the individual's destiny to "become who they
are." (Book III, §275). The difference between: (the
incongruence stemming from the difference between an
individual's view of itself, from itself) and (the individual's
view of itself, as it *supposes* it is seen from the point of view
of culture and society). This incongruence is a kind of "bad
faith" in one's self that functions as a catalyst for
"inauthenticity." Thus, to fulfill the destiny to become who
one is, is to ascend to the *Amor Fati*, and – in breaking this
seal – conquer the prize of the joyful quest.

---

[20] This comes from my *Full Throttle Heart*: "Because this book represents the
kind of "conquest" of love described in the songs of the "Knight-Poets" – "that
unity of singer, knight, and free spirit." (cf. *Ecce Homo*). In this way, *Amor Fati*
represents a kind of culmination and ecstatic moment in the Knight-Poet's quest
for joyousness."

[21] Fate is necessary; destiny is potential.

On the other hand, recall Nietzsche's comments from *Ecce Homo: How One Becomes What One Is* (1888), especially, the chapter "Why I Am So Clever," §10.

> My formula for greatness is *amor fati*: that you do not want anything to be different, not forwards, not backwards, not for all eternity. Not just to tolerate *necessity* [emphasis added], still less to conceal it ... but to *love* it...

Read in terms of Simulation theory, then, the Eternal Return as "a test" may be understood as characterizing the gradated soteriology of enlightenment discussed above. In such a context, Amor Fati may be understood not merely as the mark of the accomplishment of transcending the Simulation, but also a recipe for not being "carried along" by a Simulation. In other words, it may be understood as a recipe for an individual to "unplug" from an Actual Simulation.

Chapter 2: Virtual Simulation

Dr. Pittman

Virtual Simulation is the second type of Simulation to consider. To say the Simulation is Virtual is not to suggest it is less real. Virtual describes what it is to have a virtualized coupling between base reality and the Simulation. The form of coupling is a one-to-many relationship between a base reality machine and Simulations. The direction of the one-to-many relationship is important because it reveals the origins of the input to the relation.

Continuing with our Set Theory conceptual framework, Virtual Simulation is a second-order subset. Meaning, Virtual Simulation in relation to Actual Simulation is the same as the set of integers to the set of real numbers. It is a nested proper subset. We will explore how the Machines nests a Virtual Simulation within a hypervisor as we progress through the chapter.

For now, I want to mention second-order subsets have a capacity for strangeness. Virtual Simulation has the same capacity. For example, in *The Matrix* films, humans bend natural law within the Simulation. They bend time. They fly. They fight with superhuman speed and agility. In Virtual Simulation, since we can bend natural law and are not breaking it, there is no reason to suspect the Simulation could not manifest such things.

§1 Virtual Simulation: Universal Level of Resolution

The Universal level of Virtual Simulation implies the Machine simulates the Universal set. All things in Virtual Simulation first exist in base reality. However, such things might not be identical to their base reality counterpart.

Using numbers for example again, consider how the Integer 1 maps to an infinite range of Real numbers (i.e., 1.1, 1.1.1, 1.2, 1.3, and so forth). The integer 1 is at once the same as the Real number 1.1.2 but also not identical. There is more than meets the eye in this elementary example too.

There are two differences relative to the Actual Simulation counterpart. First, because the Simulation is Virtual, there may be multiple Simulations running concurrently. This is the one-to-many relationship. Second, a Virtual Simulation can be a remixed instantiation of base reality inputs. That is, the Virtual Simulation can have elements or details that are not present in base reality. Yet, the remixed elements or details cannot violate the natural laws inherited from base reality, only bend them.

The experience of participating in the Simulation defines the Virtual type. Suffice to say this is a literal interpretation of living in a video game. The video game is the base reality Universal set rendered into Simulation. Therefore, we can conceptualize participation as the actions and behaviors of a Player Character (PC) in first-person. Already this gives us some hint as to how the Virtual might be materially different from Actual Simulation.

§1.1 How?

Following the PC idea, we can visualize departure from the Actual-Universal type by considering the player as a Virtual artifact in contrast to an Actual PC artifact. The experience is first-person oriented. The Simulation would render observation of the PC experiencing the Simulation from the PC's viewpoint (Fig. 3).

Fig. 3: The simulated Player Character views the Universal Simulation

I want the visual to rest while we work through a couple of points. Virtual Simulation at the Universal level of resolution is a proper subset of the base reality Universal set. The distinction between subset (Actual) and proper subset (Virtual) is straightforward. Subsets contain all the elements from the set and a proper subset does not. The difference leads to downstream variations in the substrate, virtualization architecture, and input-output filtering.

I mentioned in the introduction to this chapter that there was more than meets the eye with the number analogy. The analogy works to illustrate how Virtual Simulation (Integers) is a proper subset of the Actual (Real) type. The overlap between the two illustrates how the substrate and virtualization artifacts work to generate the Virtual-Universal Simulation.

Virtual Simulation at the Universal level of resolution is as substrate dependent as Actual Simulation. The difference is a Type 1.5 hypervisor couples to a Virtual Simulation and not to the physical substrate. The hypervisor is acting as a second-order substrate. Therefore, the coupling sits between the Type 1.5 hypervisor as substrate and the Simulation. Meanwhile, the coupling between same hypervisor and the physical substrate riding atop the machine in base reality could be looser.

The looseness is the result of part of the substrate for the Simulation is itself simulated. The hypervisor is a module embedded in the substrate, rather than a discrete computational object. The integration zone between substrate and hypervisor module is ambiguous. This is not a terrible thing, though.

The benefit of a looser coupling is a single Machine can instantiate many Simulations. A hypervisor intermediary can distribute concurrent Simulations across a common architecture. An additional effect of the Virtual-Universal substrate and Type 1.5 hypervisor relationship is instantiated Simulations would necessarily be of the same type and resolution.

In this manner, we can picture Virtual Simulation as a one-dimensional geometric object. The object is a line in at least three parts (Fig. 4). On one end of the line is the base reality Machine and substrate proper. The line itself represents the Type 1.5 hypervisor and virtualization architecture. Then, at the other end of the line is the instantiated Simulation. If additional Simulations are instantiated, such would appear as additional nodes on the line.

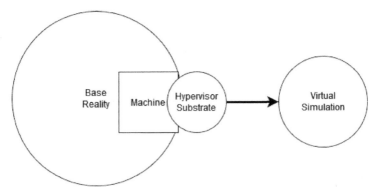

Fig. 4: The relationship between Machine, hypervisor-substrate, and the Virtual Simulation

It is worth reiterating Virtual Simulation is a proper subset. The Simulation does not simulate the entirety of the base reality universe. There are elements in base reality that are not present in the Simulation. Yet, we are operating at the level of Universal resolution which indicates to me that the input aperture is wide open. Therefore, there must be some degree of input or output filtering taking place.

I am going to take an educated guess here. I think the Machine filters input in the Virtual-Universal Simulation type. The guess is safe because computationally it would not make sense to filter output. It is much more efficient to filter before the Simulation Function receives the input and begins processing. A neat way to conceptualize the input-output pipeline in this context is as streams and not discrete chunks. The Machine streams input from base reality as contiguous content. Then, the filter is in position between the input aperture and the Simulation Function.

The filter removes base reality elements not necessary or desired for input into the Simulation Function. There are computational instruments which could achieve dynamic filtering against an input stream. Regular expressions[22] serve as a foundation in computing. Programming language design relies on them. Software often implements regular expressions for efficient data handling. Further, regular expressions excel at interacting with data streams. Thus, regular expressions are the most likely instrument. This leaves us wondering what remains as input for the Simulation Function.

§1.2 What

There is enormous overlap between Actual and Virtual Simulation types. There is enough difference to warrant separate categorization though. Right away we know the input from base reality is not identical between the types. We also know we are dealing with a different architectural arrangement with the Type 1.5 hypervisor. However, we don't know what is different within the resultant Simulation. Much of this section will focus on those differences. At the same time, we also need to draw out the parallels if we are going to develop reliable guide stones using these artifacts.

---

[22] A regular expression is a pattern matching instrument. For example, the regular expression [+−]? (\d + (\.\d *)? |\.\d+)([eE][+−]?\d+)? will detect any numeral in a stream of input.

We established the Actual-Universal Simulation as having effectively zero variance. In contrast, the Virtual-Universal Simulation could have minor details vary between instantiations. The Type 1.5 hypervisor serving as the proxy substrate could introduce minor variation into the Simulation. As well, the input filter might select minor details between instantiations of the same Virtual-Universal Simulation.

Reasoning from these points, I think the differences are insignificant. The differences represent minor degrees of variation. The Virtual universe would *appear* similar enough to be identical. However, this is true from a vantage point located in base reality. To gauge comparable effects within the Simulation, we need to consider whether glitches occur and are perceptible.

Put simply, change to the instantiated Simulation, initiated from base reality by the Programmer, would be possible. Moreover, I suspect the degree of glitching may be perceptible in a peripheral sense. I don't know if this implies a form of *déjà vu* though. I think if *déjà vu* fits as a concept, we must take it as a general, non-specific term. Considering we now have noticeable repetition or changes inside the Simulation, I think it would be helpful to understand what makes this possible.

The reason repetition or change were not possible in Actual-Universal is due to the tight coupling between Machine and Simulation. With Virtual Simulation, the coupling is looser because of the Type 1.5 hypervisor. Accordingly, and this is true with modern virtualization today, there are methods to update the Machine, substrate, and hypervisor which in turn could manifest repetition or change to elements within the Simulation. I think of this as *unintentional glitching*.

Conversely, I don't think there is an opportunity for *intentional glitching*. It would not be possible to force a glitch. The Simulation is not a playground or experimental vessel. I don't think this is true because I'm naïve to the potential motivation of the Programmer. The Programmer's motivation is unknowable in fact. Instead, I'm confident the coupling between a Type 1.5 hypervisor and the Machine-substrate would exist in such a manner that the Simulation would dissolve under intentional glitching.

The fidelity of the Virtual-Universal Simulation may be sufficiently indistinguishable from base reality albeit with some loss. The loss may not be immediately detectable within the Virtual Simulation. We need to examine where the fidelity malfunctions might occur to be certain.

We can continue with the TV analogy we started when discussing Actual-Individual Simulation. That is, the TV continues to function as a television. It receives an input signal on one medium, converts the signal internally, and then renders the content out into a visible resolution. All is not the same, though.

With Virtual-Universal, the substrate is not physical. Rather, the internal signal-to-resolution conversion is occurring through a Virtual substrate. We are close to how Virtual-Universal Simulation renders fidelity when we imagine a small TV inside of our large TV. The resolution is still a bit for bit, pixel for pixel, replication of base reality but rendered through an extra component.

The error rate and accuracy of Virtual Simulation at the Universal level of resolution would be the sum of all Actual Simulation resolutions. This is a fair generalization when we consider the Virtual substrate to be equivalent to the base reality Machine with addons. The addon of the hypervisor shifts Simulation elements between backdrop and Simulation. The Simulation Function and hypervisor render the Simulation into the Virtual substrate. In other words, the added Virtual Simulation components introduce a loss of accuracy that is noticeable. Likewise, error rates are perceptible in this case because of the increased computational demand of upscaled resolution. The error rates here in Virtual-Universal have more to do with the Virtual substrate than anything else.

Oddly enough, I do not think the Programmer would necessarily observe further degradation of Simulation precision compared to prior Simulation types. I would argue the introduction of the hypervisor-as-substrate would introduce additional precision controls. The hypervisor yields additional controls. It also represents expanded computational capability. This stands to reason given the capability of Virtual Simulation at the Universal level of resolution to be rendered as precisely as the base reality universe.

Be that as it may, due to the one-to-many nature of the Virtual, the Simulations have less capability. The additional hypervisor computational overhead is the cause. For comparison, if an Actual-Universal Simulation is 100% capable, Virtual-Universal is 99.999% capable of simulating base reality. This includes the representations, behaviors, and interactions therein.

§1.3 When?

Overall, I don't imagine *when* in the Simulation to be significantly different in the Virtual-Universal case. The reason I suspect this is true is due to the computational interconnection between the Machine, physical substrate, and hypervisor substrate.

I think this works like *threading* in computing. That is, if we imagine a program to exists as a thread then we can say that a computational function processes threads. More aptly we can assert that computational functions operate on input as part of a thread. These threads work at two levels: kernel and user. The difference between two is the layer of operation wherein the thread executes. Given the idea of threading, it is the case a single kernel level thread runs the Virtual Simulation at the Universal level of resolution.

In doing so, we are in proper alignment with the one-to-many concept too. That is, one kernel level thread possesses the connection to the one virtualization layer and in turn the virtualization may instantiate many Simulations. Concurrently, all instantiated Simulations share a common, Universal *when* artifact in terms of tick rate without constraints on thread management or thread pinning.

§1.4 Constraints

The same constraints from the Actual type of Simulation apply to Virtual-Universal context. We must add an additional layer because of the hypervisor though. On one hand base reality natural law still constrains the Simulation. On the other hand, the hypervisor is not entirely situated in base reality as is the Machine or the Simulation Function. Rather, the hypervisor spans between base reality and the Simulation. As a result, the hypervisor rendering natural law from base reality into Virtual natural law constrains the Simulation.

With respect to specific constraints such as compute resources, signaling, and integrity check, I suspect we will find the implementation of the constraints to be different. I also think constraints are an area where we can see the evidence of functional trade-off through interoperability and extensibility of the Simulation architecture.

It should not take more energy to run a Virtual-Universal simulated compared to the Actual type at any level of resolution. Natural law still constrains the Simulation. Likewise, a Virtual-Universal Simulation does not require more storage. The logic here holds because we are operating within the context of a proper subset. There are *less* elements in the Simulation compared to the Actual-Universal. While the difference in elements may not be significant, it would be enough to keep the energy and storage constraints the same.

However, there might be a need for more compute power. The Machine needs more power because of the increase in computation taking place through the hypervisor. As well, the Machine is performing *more* computation. The additional compute power need not come from more energy though. The hypervisor-substrate might introduce an efficiency allowing for the same total energy. The Machine could simply be more powerful for the same energy input.

There is a foundational complexity introduced with the Type 1.5 hypervisor which leads to a minor alteration in the signaling-communication constraint. More specifically, the signaling-communication between a base reality Machine Simulation Function and the Simulation side of the hypervisor transits a bottleneck. There is a possibility for loss and delay at the bottleneck. The solution is for either side to implement forward and backward congestion signaling. As a simple example of this constraint, think about a water pipe narrowing at a connection junction. A pressure sensor could signal modulation of water flow control.

The constraints related to interoperability and extensibility benefit from the change in Simulation substrate. For instance, virtual machines can be migrated between hypervisors on the same physical host or even across different physical hosts belonging to the same cluster of systems. The hypervisor must be identical though if such interoperability is to function correctly. Concurrently, because the physical substrate is virtualized, the components exposed upstream into the Simulation are also virtualized. This means the Machine can change components without negatively affecting the Simulation.

The Type 1.5 hypervisor uses hashing to verify the integrity of the Virtual-Universal Simulation. This is because the hypervisor is the Virtual-Universal component with functional control over input, function, and output. While the Machine physical substrate could perform integrity checking as well, such would be premature given how the hypervisor-substrate is responsible for instantiating elements form base reality into Simulation.

With that said, the operational constructs associated with integrity checking remain the same for the input-output pairing. I will point out the integrity of the running Simulation becomes more critical in relation to the increase in interoperability. If we migrate a Simulation to another hypervisor-substrate, we will want to know such a Simulation is in the same state after the movement. Thus, the value of integrity increases.

§2 Virtual Simulation: Social Level of Resolution

In contrast to Virtual-Universal, the Social level of resolution exists in the same manner as Actual-Social Simulation. The Simulation is based on social interaction and societal constructions. However, in the Actual type we observed a physical substrate generate the Simulation. Now, in the Virtual type, we are dealing with a virtualized substrate atop a Type 1.5 hypervisor. Thus, I don't think we can consider the Social artifact to be the same perspective of participation in society as Actual Simulation.

Instead, actions and behaviors oriented in third person drive the Virtual-Social perspective. The effect is akin to a Player Character (PC) in massively multiplayer online role-playing game (MMORPG) played in third-person perspective (Fig. 5). The departure from Virtual-Universal is a matter of point-of-view. We are still in a video game. The difference is a disembodied observer translates our experience. Let's draw this out and see how the change in perspective is manifested.

Fig. 5: The Virtual Simulation experienced as a 3rd Person Player Character

§2.1 How?

In terms of Set Theory, a Virtual Simulation at the Social level of resolution continues the proper subset form. As a proper subset the Virtual-Social Simulation lacks elements from the base reality universal set. Specifically, there are base reality social norms, mores, and constructs absent from the Simulation. Furthermore, whereas I speculated there were two exclusive explanations for how the Social level of resolution works in the Actual type, I believe the same two explanations exist in the Virtual type. There is an aperture and there is a form of Selection Function. The latter is what affects the proper subset configuration and exists in the substrate.

We know given the Simulation type there are some aspects of the physical substrate not simulated through the Type 1.5 hypervisor. In other words, the Virtual-Social Simulation is a proper subset. We expected no less of course. I mention this at the risk of being repetitive because the Virtual-Universal Simulation effectively has two substrates. One substrate is the physical, Actual substrate. The second is the Type 1.5 hypervisor. However, we should consider Virtual-Social to have a single substrate.

This may feel like a regression. Instead, I argue it is convergence. This is the case when take from the Simulation perspective rather than the base reality view. Indeed, the substrate and the hypervisor bind the Social level of resolution. There is no awareness or sense of connectedness to the physical Machine substrate. We should recall this is how Actual-Social Simulation is instantiated. The difference is now the instantiation is one layer deeper. The instantiation is divorced from the Machine itself.

As well, we now have a Selection Function working in concert with the input aperture. Because of the substrate architecture, I think the Selection Function implementation is likely to be in the physical substrate. First, the Selection Function is either adjacent to or embedded in the Simulation Function. Therefore, the physical substrate would be the architectural location most fitting. Further, selection is a computational algorithm. The goal is for the algorithm to subdivide a greater object. The Selection Function loads before the Virtual-Social Simulation.

The geometric line illustrates the hypervisor and loaded Simulation relationship. The line reveals a minor alteration, however (Fig. 6). While a node on the line continues to represent an instantiated Virtual Simulation, the node can extend a short, terminated line upwards. By doing so, the Virtual Simulation geometrically establishes a subdivision for the Social level of resolution across the substrate fabric (i.e., line). The geometry also begins to take on a two-dimensional shape now with both x and y axes present.

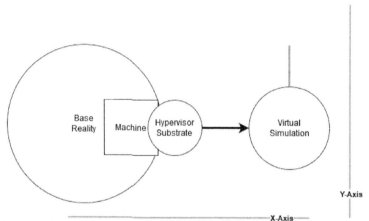

Fig. 6. The addition of a second spatial dimension in the geometry of the Virtual Simulation

We know the Virtual Simulation type uses a Type 1.5 hypervisor. The virtualization architecture ends there for the Universal level of resolution because the hypervisor instantiates a complete Simulation. Computationally, there is nothing outside of the universe. I am tempted to let the same idea carry forward here in the Social level of resolution, especially since we identified the hypervisor substrate is more or less a singular, unified structure. However, the Simulation demands more of us. We must push deeper if we are going to understand the implementation of the virtualization artifact in the Virtual-Social context.

The virtualization architecture requires more due to the tight coupling of the virtualized Simulation to the hypervisor instead of the physical substrate. The importance of the architectural difference is not evident here except for the utmost technical of details. Instead, the differences are upstream in other artifacts. Suffice it to say, one immediate difference compared to the Actual Type 1 hypervisors is that Virtual-Social Simulation can instantiate subcomponents that appear physical but are completely virtualized.

Thus, virtualization at this level of resolution resembles a nested compartment or container within an outer Type 1.5 hypervisor. If we call back the car and driving example I developed in the Actual-Social Simulation section, we can now imagine the equivalent of the experiencing of driving, the car, and the road all back into a single virtualized stack but not tied to a physical substrate. That is, the entire scene is Virtual.

With such a substrate architecture, I don't see why the Type 1.5 hypervisor could not support a concurrent mix of Virtual-Universal and Virtual-Social Simulations. If so, the architecture moves the input aperture from the base reality Machine input mechanism to the hypervisor. We should not underestimate the significance of such a modification. The consequence is Universal input passes through the Machine, the Simulation Function, into the physical substrate, and finally the hypervisor itself.

§2.2 What?

We have a taste for how the Virtual Simulation type diverges from the Actual, at least in the Universal resolution context. Like the Universal resolution, I suspect we will find quite a bit of overlap at the Social level too. Certainly, this is true insofar as *what is being simulated* is simulated to a degree that the Simulation is reality. The Simulation is realistic to its inhabitants at least at the Social level of resolution. I also think we will find the degrees of difference start to deviate more substantially. Imagine a vector as opposed to a straight line.

From the base reality view of the Virtual-Social Simulation there would be variance in the Simulation. The variance appears only under scrutiny though. My first guess would pinpoint the substrate and virtualization architecture as culprits. While true, I do not believe those Simulation artifacts cause the variance. Rather, when I look deeper, I can see how the Selection Function is more responsible for variance in the Simulation across instantiations.

If the Selection Function selected identical elements for every instantiation, there would no difference between Virtual-Social Simulations. The effective outcome would be an Actual Simulation and not a Virtual type. For clarity, what I see holds for the same Simulation over iterations of instantiation as well as for multiple instances of Virtual-Social Simulations running concurrently.

Changes to the runtime environment are possible as a result of the how Virtual-Social Simulation is instantiated. The Programmer could select active Social elements, inject a modified version, and the Social Simulation would take on the update. Alternatively, and not exclusively mind you, the Programmer could preconfigure a Social element change through the Simulation Function for a future time. To the hypervisor-substrate, the input would be no different than any other. Yet, within the Simulation, the change is a real time event and noticeable.

On the contrary, if the Programmer where to inject the same element over top of itself (i.e., repetition), I do not think the Simulation would experience the change. At least not 100% of the time. Despite being the Simulation being more specific at this level of resolution compared to the Universal, there is enough abstraction remaining to shroud repetition. Exceptions may occur, however. If exceptions manifest, the Virtual-Social Simulation would experience the repetition.

On that note, we can use fidelity to identify measures relative to what the Virtual-Social simulates. A one-to-many relation defines the Virtual type. The undergirding is computational and necessarily so. In all aspects of resolution, the Virtual-Social Simulation is identical to the Virtual-Universal error rates, accuracy, and precision.

Granted, the resolution is narrower and that is why we have a distinct Virtual-Social artifact. However, beyond this I do not see anything to suggest the Simulation has a different error rate or accuracy than the Universal level of resolution. The most I can say is the small TV resolution within the larger TV tunes to the level of the Social.

Indeed, from the perspective of the Simulation, a Social stimulus directed towards itself would elicit social experience equivalent to Actual Simulation. Conversely, I suspect Social interaction with the general Simulation backdrop might induce slight variation in sensitivity. The non-computational description of this phenomenon is, *something is not right, but I cannot put my finger on it.* Computationally, this is like mapping a continuous value vector in one space to a discrete value vector in an adjacent space[23].

§2.3 When?

The Virtual Simulation exists relative to base reality through *when*. We would be discussing Actual Simulation if we stopped with the Simulation and time one-to-one relationship. However, in the Virtual Simulation *when* also exists relative to the hypervisor and virtualization

---

[23] This is a hackneyed explanation of a linear algebra process. My intent is to illustrate how it might be possible to lose fidelity in a number during the process of moving it from one space to another.

constructs. In addition, I suggest on one hand, the Virtual-Social Simulation progresses linearly. The progress is in lockstep with the base reality timeline. On the other hand, the experience of participation in social constructs can decouple time within the Simulation from the base reality.

Furthermore, decoupled implies nonlinear within the context of the Social Simulation. The decoupling certainly could manifest between a Simulation and the non-Simulation backdrop. More likely, I think the decoupling and nonlinearity would be apparent in the computational space between hypervisor substrate, virtualization, and many Virtual-Social Simulations. Unlike with the Virtual-Universal Simulation, the Social artifact of *when* is firmly situated within an extended one-to-many context insofar as there are a multitude of societies possible, a multitude of social interactions within each. Computationally, I believe two mechanisms would be necessary to implement and manage the Virtual-Social *when*.

First, the Virtual type carries forward the idea of threading into a multithreading domain. Specifically, the Social Simulation has a dedicated thread in the hypervisor-virtualization stack as does the non-Social backdrop. This allows for the backdrop to be common across all social Simulations. Simultaneously, the Virtual-Social Simulation inherits from a single kernel level thread running the Virtual to become a single child level thread.

As well, each the hypervisor-substrate pins the Social Simulation to its thread much in the same manner as Actual-Social. Naturally, the difference here is the extended linkage back through the virtualization layer, the hypervisor substrate, to the physical substrate in the base reality Machine. As such, constraints interact with Virtual-Social Simulation dissimilarly.

§2.4 Constraints

The constraints applicable to Virtual-Social Simulation bring with them the logic developed thus far throughout the Actual type as well as Virtual-Universal Simulation. That is, there are constraints on the Simulation stemming from the natural laws in base reality as well as the hypervisor driving the Virtual type rendering Virtual natural law. Such rendering of the natural into the Virtual is straightforward at the Universal level of resolution. However, the Social resolution constraints manifest differently because we have introduced a layer of virtualization with a Type 1.5 hypervisor. The nature of the input has changed too. Thus, I think the constraints themselves are different compared to the Actual and Virtual-Universal types as well as the implementation.

We should consider the compute resource constraints as scaling to the focal point of the Virtual-Social proper subset. Thus, we should anticipate much of the same given how compute power, energy, and storage functioned at the Universal level of resolution. However, just as there was some meaningful difference from Actual to Virtual, we have some room to investigate the nuanced differences with Virtual-Social compute resource constraints too.

Case in point, storage constraints may change to accommodate links to single Social source copies instead of allowing full copies. This requires less storage. This does increase the compute overhead because of the need to track the links and associated metadata. Energy and compute power, hand in hand, need to allocated between the backdrop and foreground Simulation. Typically, the level of compute resource management required in such cases indicates the need for a schedular program or task orchestration. The location of such functionality is flexible. The Machine might abstract the functionality into the emergent complexity of the Simulation architecture for instance.

Indeed, there is a foundational complexity introduced both with the Type 1.5 hypervisor and the logical separation of backdrop and Simulation. Put simply, whereas the Virtual-Universal signaling and communication is a water pipe with a bottleneck at a handoff junction, the Virtual-Social is a T-joint. Let me explain.

The evolution of this constraint reflects the development of the Simulation logic. To that end, the T-joint junction takes the base reality input signaling and splits it into two feeds. I think that much is obvious given the analogy. Be that as it may, I don't see that as necessarily the cause of the complexity. The complexity comes from needing to select which elements belong to which signal-communication stream. Additional complexity arises from the return signaling and communications need to be identifiable within the stream bundle returning from the two arms into the hypervisor-substrate.

The separation, tracking, and reassembly of signal-communications are all achievable. The constraint can leverage the existing architecture to insert tags at the element level from the Selection Function. As well, the hypervisor can run a recognition component to manage the return stream. Easy enough but there is a side effect.

Interoperability and extensibility are the constraints where the side effect manifests. Instinctively, we might consider the side effect to be a reduced capability to interoperate across different hypervisor-substrates of the same type. Further, we might suspect the signaling-communication complexity to constrain extensibility back to a level of the Actual. While possible, sure, I don't think these are the side effect consequences.

The fact is, any Machine sufficiently advanced to produce a Virtual-Social Simulation will be sufficiently capable of modularizing its architecture. Meaning, at worst, the side effect forces the T-joint logic into a discrete component. By doing so, interoperability and extensibility increased. Thus, the Machine abstracts complexity into components and loosely couples those components to the overall architecture.

I am close to believing integrity checking is necessary at the interaction level. In other words, every Social construct producing or receiving an interaction ought to have an integrity characteristic for each transaction. The constraint would need to operate throughout the virtualization stack as well as within the input-output streams. However, I don't think this kind of integrity checking is quite necessary yet.

Alternatively, I think the rational implementation of the constraint continues to be at the hypervisor-substrate, on the Simulation side of the artifact. This would be the only location in the architecture where the hypervisor-substrate checks integrity. As well, the hypervisor-substrate can measure integrity of the backdrop and the Simulation separately and as a cohesive whole.

§3 Virtual Simulation: Individual Level of Resolution

Many of us have at least a fuzzy idea of what virtual reality is; the almost-real like video gaming experience requiring us to wear special goggles or headsets. Additionally, immersive video gaming experiences such as Minecraft, World of Warcraft, and Elder Scrolls Skyrim have left an indelible mark as *virtual* societies.

Sticking with the video game analogy, Virtual Simulation at the level of resolution of the Individual is still a MMORPG albeit locked into a first-person perspective. In other words, we are no longer controlling an avatar in a virtual world as much as we are participating in the virtual world firsthand. The change in perspective forces a realignment of input across the hypervisor-substrate such that the experience of others amounts to participation in a society and participation in a society amounts to participation in the Virtual-Social Simulation.

To be clear, we are still dealing with a proper subset and a one-to-many relation between base reality and simulated elements. However, I think there are architectural differences related to the switch from third-person to first-person perspective worth our attention. If I had to guess ahead, I suppose we will encounter more difference in the Simulation going forward.

§3.1 How?

The most significant deviation in the Simulation thus far has been the transition to a Type 1.5 hypervisor and the inclusion of a substrate Selection Function. Virtual Simulation at the Individual level of resolution retains those concepts while introducing a set of new features related to *nesting*. I first introduced the idea of nesting when outlining the overarching Actual-Individual Simulation type but balked at implementing the idea. However, I think Virtual-Individual is the right time to bring nesting to the foreground.

The substrate for Virtual Simulation at the Individual level of resolution is itself simulated but only partially. I suggest partially because of the Type 1.5 hypervisor which is something we are quite familiar with at this point. Moving on, we have the Virtual-Individual substrate as a Simulation instantiated by the hypervisor. This nesting of substrates is something new and thus bears exploring.

If we recall, I had mentioned earlier, during the Actual-Individual discussion, that nesting was a computational option capable of producing the type and resolution. While nesting could have made sense in that case, I see nesting as a more natural technique to achieve Individual resolution in the Virtual type. The justification is straightforward: I do not see another way to produce an Individual Simulation as a proper subset without nesting the Individual in an outer backdrop Simulation.

If the Individual is adjacent to the backdrop, we are back to having the Individual as a collective as in the Actual and Virtual types. Alternatively, if we nest the Simulation substrate in a backdrop substrate, well then, we have the potential for a multitude of singular Individual

Simulations. This exemplifies a one-to-one-to-many relation, but it also preserves the Individual proper subset.

Lastly, I think the Selection Function is still operational at this level of Simulation resolution. Instead of residing in the physical, Machine substrate though I can see the rationale for the selective algorithm to run somewhere between the two hypervisors. I realize how this breaks the pattern of modifying or otherwise filtering input close the source. However, because we are dealing with the simulated Individual, and the Individual is sufficiently more complex as a level of resolution, it makes sense to maximize the input and select at the point of Simulation runtime. Doing so permits a wider array of instantiation options particularly when they may be a battery of concurrent Simulations running.

In terms of virtualization, the Individual level of resolution seems to me to be a Type 1.5 hypervisor nested within an .5 hypervisor. The latter, again, is a module attached to the base reality Machine physical substrate or kernel. Virtualization as it applies to the Simulation is three layers removed from base reality. This is something like real universe, Virtual universe, Virtual society, and then Virtual individual all consecutively nested.

The distance from one substrate to the last hypervisor is not important per se. Distance is an effective means to describe the virtualization stack though. Architectural distance then is valuable to us because it sets boundaries for the Virtual-Individual context. On one hand, the nesting of hypervisors in this manner creates a more flexible, a more loosely coupled architecture. Yet, on the other hand, nesting introduces complexity and single points of failure across the series of hypervisor-substrates.

There would not be a computational barrier to limit the Individual's interactions because of the hypervisor nesting. There would be increasing computational overhead through each nested layer. I can imagine how input-output filtering might help overcome a portion of the loss in compute resources as the nesting goes deeper though.

Foremost, the Simulation aperture at the base reality input would need to be maximally open. I think closing the aperture down to a Social or Individual diameter would be unduly limit the range of Simulation possibilities. Upstream, at the point of input to the origin Type 1.5 hypervisor, there would be the Actual-Individual filter along with a Virtual-Individual filter.

The combination of filters allows for a sieving or titration of Individual elements without limiting the base reality input. In this way, once the Simulation reaches the endpoint hypervisor for Simulation, only those elements necessary for the Virtual-Individual Simulation are available. With such an input-output filtering architecture, we might be able to have a mix of Simulation types running concurrently from the origin hypervisor as we speculated might be possible in the Virtual-Social artifact.

§3.2 What?

Just like that we are back to the Individual as the focal point of the Simulation. On one hand we are the farthest away from where the Virtual Simulation type began. Yet, on the other hand, we are at the potential limits of what a Type 1.5 hypervisor can manifest into a Simulation. We may find interesting artifacts at the Individual extreme.

Whereas one Virtual-Individual Simulation need not be the same as any other, even a second instantiation of itself, I contend the computational demands of this level of resolution renders the Simulation such that it can never be the identical. Further, variance exists to the extent that differences between successive instantiations of Simulation are immediately evident to viewers in base reality but with the feeling of a false memory of sorts.

Imagine putting your car keys on a table after coming home from work. Could you tell if one key was a millimeter askew when you reached for the keys in the morning? I think not, you'll agree. This degree of variance would be more associated with Virtual-Social Simulation. Now, suppose the keys are facing the opposite direction from how recall setting them down. I reckon you would notice this but quickly dismiss the thought as spurious recollection.

Not only would change be possible, but changes might also be uncontrollable. Likewise, the Virtual-Individual Simulation can manifest repetition bot planned and unplanned. Both change and repetition within an instantiated Simulation would be immediately experienced. This is the black cat walking past the doorway twice. This is the bricked-up window that was just a moment ago transparent glass. In other words, any interaction between the Virtual-Individual and the Simulation creates an opportunity for experiential glitches.

We have discussed the Programmer and intentional change or repetition in previous Virtual Simulation types. The principles we outlined in those types and resolutions carry forward to here. Conversely, we now also have the ability for the Individual to create events indistinguishable from Programmer originating change and repetition based on its (invisible) nested architecture. In some fashion, I imagine a Virtual-Individual interaction being like a ripple on a body of water; the ripple may proceed unhindered until it expends all its energy, or it may collide with another ripple, even itself.

Computationally, there are a myriad of conditions that may arise in these complex, nested architectures. From race conditions caused by resource competition across threaded processes, to perturbation of data relationships based on downstream element changes, the idea of fragility is not without merit.

In addition to any such fragility, the fidelity of this type and resolution of Simulation would be mutable. More specifically, the fidelity is apt to change relative to the Individual. In this way, fidelity becomes somewhat of a weather vane, revealing more about the state of the Virtual-Individual Simulation than just resolution, error rates, accuracy, and so forth.

For instance, we know resolution is a measure of the degree to which the granularity of the Simulation aligns with the source. In Actual Simulation, the source was base reality itself. Therefore, the Simulation displayed at least as much detail as the physical universe. However, in Virtual Simulation we have a partially virtualized source. Thus, some of the source is not based on physical reality.

Computationally, this tells us synthetic values partially makeup the resolution of the Virtual-Individual Simulation. In other words, the binary value 0 (zero) is a value synthetically constructed by the Virtual substrate to *match* a corresponding binary value in base reality. To compound this effect, it might be possible that each mote of resolution is a synthetic construction of Individual formatted interactions.

In simple terms, this is each pixel in the TV resolution synthetically rendered individually. The reference is base reality, but the rendering is not direct from the source. The small TV inside (the Virtual substrate) is full of these synthetic Individual pixels.

I must imagine the rate of errors is significantly higher because of (a) the alignment of the hypervisor-substrate and (b) lack of integration or adjacency awareness between pixels in the TV resolution. We know the extra compute overhead increases error rates, thus decreasing accuracy. Unlike the Virtual-Social context though, I suspect the Individual resolution demand for synthetic resolution and levels of variance, repetition, and frequency of interaction adds to the error rate.

Conversely, I cannot imagine the rate of error and accompanying reduction in accuracy goes unnoticed. This isn't the keys are facing the wrong direction from where we left them on the table. This is the keys are not at all in the same place. Dismissible as bad memory, sure, but ever more noticeable and suspect.

Certainly, the suspicion of errors in the simulated Virtual-Individual reality stems from the hypervisor-substrate. There is an intuition here which might lead us to conclude the fidelity is related to a drop off in compute resources and thus fidelity. However, I think the related sense of something being off increases in conjunction with drop in accuracy has more to do with the increase in necessary sensitivity and precision. The Individual level of resolution cannot benefit from the focal diffusion represented in the Social or Universal aperture width.

§3.3 When?

In terms of *when*, the Individual level of resolution within a Virtual type gives us our first glimpse into real computational complexity. The complexity arises because the Virtual-Individual computational implementation of *when* is a classical one-to-many multithreading architecture.

Foremost, one thread runs the Simulation backdrop. A second thread exists which we can refer to as *individuals*. This, unlike Virtual-Universal or Virtual-Social, is not the primary Simulation thread though. Rather, each instantiation of the Individual requires a distinct and separate *when* artifact. Thus, every Individual is spawned from the *individuals* thread onto its own child thread which then process simultaneously relative to (a) one another, (b) the backdrop, (c) and in step to the inherited base reality tick rate.

As we might suppose, the first and second simultaneous relations are tricky but not insurmountably so when considering computational complexity. Even in modern computation, a scheduler[24] process- our *individuals*

---

[24] A scheduler oversees the total pool of process threads in memory and manages compute resource allocation across that pool.

thread- can handle rather advanced processing patterns over time. Be that as it may, the relation between the *individuals* scheduler, each Individual, and the base reality tick rate is decidedly more tenuous.

Even with process pinning, as we head towards the Mental type of Simulation, tick rate drift between the multitude of Individual threads is inevitable. If these threads were short-lived, temporal decoupling would not be an issue. However, over long thread lifetimes and especially under high computer power loading, the Individual perception of time within the Simulation will desynchronize from other Individuals, from the Simulation backdrop, and assuredly from the base reality reference tick rate.

§3.4 Constraints

We must keep in mind the operational context for the constraints associated with the Virtual-Individual Simulation. Foremost, the prior two levels of resolution impart constraints on this type of Simulation. While the previous levels of resolution bring forth the notion of virtualized natural law, the Virtual-Individual Simulation establishes nested artifacts. Consequently, even if the constraints at this level of Simulation are functionally identical, implementation and interaction with them cannot be the same.

At the same time, the constraints also apply uniquely to the Individual resolution because of the nesting of substrates. In fact, the uniqueness might be such that constraints become a spectrum of continuous values as opposed to the discrete implementation as observed in the preceding Simulation artifacts. I suspect we will find the addition of constraint spectrums affects a few of the constraint artifacts more than others.

The Virtual Simulation at the Individual level of Simulation will certainly require novel compute resource allocation compared to previous levels of Simulation resolution and types. I use *novel* instead of *more* or *additional* because our constraints are still in accordance with natural laws extending from base reality. Thus, the applied constraint here is not for *more* compute power or energy, the constraint is using the maximum amount of available compute power and energy more effectively, more efficiently.

Interestingly enough, I suspect the substrate and virtualization architecture self-enforces the compute power, energy, and storage constraint. I could see part of the Simulation Function incorporating minimal viable Simulation compute power. Energy would follow compute power insofar as the same overall demand exists, but energy is allocated to a wider array of Simulation artifacts. The architecture constrains storage similarly to Virtual-Social Simulation.

I suspect we are now at the edge of what the Virtual Simulation architecture can support. At the risk of being mildly repetitive, the plumbing analogy continues to be our best representation of signaling-communication. We want to bring forward the idea of signaling and communication using a T-joint structure to implement the backdrop and foreground Simulation. Now, let's add a second T-joint onto the Simulation side to achieve a collection and singleton Individual.

The addition of a second logical T-joint component may seem trivial. It is trivial as a constraint artifact. However, the architecture adds complexity due to the tagging and recognition associated with managing a signal and communication sub-feed. Thus, as we transition away from Virtual Simulation, I want to contemplate to what extent embedded, nested sub-processing might be necessary on the equivalent Simulation artifact.

I think interoperability might reach its highest levels yet as a result of the additional T-joint in our plumbing analogy. Everything above the hypervisor-substrate could be portable across any physical computational framework.

The sole limiting factor would be the implementation of the downstream constraints (e.g., compute power).

The price for such flexibility might be extensibility. At a broad level, the Machine and hypervisor-substrate could implement new pipe arrangements prior to Simulation instantiation. Once water is flowing though we could not swap out the same T-joint let alone make an adjustment to the angle of a joint bend.

I don't see a way around integrity checking in the Virtual-Individual Simulation occurring at the interaction level. The reason I don't see a way around this is because of the capability for the Individual to be a collective or singleton. If it were only one or the other, integrity checking would function similarly to other Simulation types and resolution. However, the integrity checking function won't work on two different artifacts with the same nature. I also don't think the architecture supports multiple implementations of integrity checking. Furthermore, the mutability of the Virtual-Individual Simulation would either break existing integrity validations or force a complete revalidation of the Simulation. The sound approach for this architecture is to compute integrity on interactions.

Dr. Scalambrino

Philosophically speaking, the "Virtual Simulation" level of resolution in Simulation theory refers to the idea that our entire experience of reality is *not actually* the experience of a Simulation, but it is *virtually* the experience of a Simulation. It is difficult to say that without seeming like one is equivocating, so here is a clarifying restatement of that thought: Whereas in Actual Simulation, actuality is understood as being a Simulation, in Virtual Simulation, actuality is not thought of as being a Simulation; actuality is where the hypervisor is found.

Thus, in the Virtual type of Simulation, actuality refers to base reality; the virtual reality of the Simulation is anchored in actuality, anchored in reality, and that Simulation is a kind of virtual reality. Therefore, "Virtual" in "Virtual Simulation" means *both* virtual as a virtual reality and virtual in contrast to actual. Further, as we will see, ontologically the difference between Virtual Simulation's levels of resolution may be best accounted for in terms of existential, economic, and technological forces.

In my personal opinion, it is in terms of Virtual Simulation that Simulation Theory may be true. On the one hand, Simulation Theory in terms of Actual Simulation may simply amount to substituting the term "Simulation" for the word "Nature," in terms Modern Western philosophy. So, I don't really see the upshot or much value in saying that Simulation Theory is true in terms of Actual Simulation. It really just sees God as a computer, and the philosophical possibilities of God as a computer were already considered by Scholastic philosophers – even if they could never have imagined an iPhone.

On the other hand, I believe it is correct to think of Simulation Theory in terms of Mental Simulation as a kind of mental illness. It is not just that Mental Simulation is solipsistic, nor is it simply that individual Simulation is narcissistic to a point beyond its own practical, or pragmatic, good. Rather, it is the obsessiveness with which it is taken up that one tends to notice first. And, all of these aspects of Mental Simulation, taken together, seem to make it simply a kind of fantasy. Yet, there are a number of ways Virtual Simulation may be a viable characterization of reality according to Simulation theory.

The best justification for the existence of such a simulated reality may be found at the social level of resolution. It would not merely be one woman or man who would be sustaining a whole Simulation. Rather, a community, a social grouping of individuals, would be needed to sustain a Simulation that enveloped them. In many ways, the lines of thought found in all of the following thinkers seem to leave open the possibility that social reality itself is a kind of Simulation that is sustained by our participation in it.

Philosophers associated with Virtual Simulation span a diverse portion of Western philosophy; they are: Martin Heidegger (1889-1976), Jacques Ellul (1912-1994), Louis Marin (1931-1992), Gilles Deleuze (1925-1995), Jean Baudrillard (1929-2007), and Theodore J. Kaczynski (1942-).[25] The point of departure, then, is Jean Baudrillard's *Simulacra and Simulation*. Referencing, Marin's excellent discussion of Disneyland, Baudrillard offers a list of the conditions by way of which a simulated society comes to exist. For example, Disneyland is a hyperreality; it is a reality, even though it is clearly a "fantasy world."

Similarly, Ellul, Deleuze, and Kaczynski emphasize how such a Simulation can be a means of control. For our purpose here, I will enumerate these as: a token system and the technological mediation of our relation to the *Welt*-matrix – that is to say, the *Um-Welt, Mit-Welt, Selbst-Welt,* and *Eigen-Welt* – that which physically surrounds us, our participation in the "with-world" or social relations to other

---

[25] Most readers will recognize the work of Nietzsche, Marx, and Foucault appear in the following discussion; however, I have chosen to remain focused on the more contemporary French and German thinkers toward being succinct.

beings, our relation to ourself (specifically as a body), and our relation to spirituality or be-ing itself.

§4 Virtual Simulation: Universal Level of Resolution

At the universal level of resolution, actuality would refer to base reality, and the Simulation would refer to a virtualization anchored in actuality. That is to say, the hypervisor responsible for the manifestation of virtual reality would be somehow rooted in base reality. Thus, Virtual Simulation may be understood from the universal level of resolution as encompassing everyone. In other words, we must distinguish between the actual and virtual aspects of the reality in which we dwell and distinguish between the Actual and Virtual dimensions of the *Um-Welt*, *Mit-Welt*, *Selbst-Welt*, and *Eigen-Welt*.

We should note three possibilities here, then. The difference between actuality as base reality and virtual reality as Simulation may be understood as neutral in value, as good in value, or as bad. Further, of course, each of these valences may have its own kind and style of justification. Though we need not flesh all of those possibilities out here in order to understand Simulation Theory, we do need to keep in mind the type of relation that makes this a discussion of Virtual Simulation. That relation is such that there is an actuality that need not participate in the virtuality. That is to say, there is an actuality that is different from the virtuality, and that means liberation from the Simulation is possible.

Though it is possible to articulate the Virtual level of Simulation in terms of the Buddhist understanding of the "skandas" or "Five Aggregates" and Plato's Cave, since that characterization was already sketched out regarding Actual Simulation, only a few words need to be said here to illuminate the transposition of the idea from the key of Actual Simulation to the key of Virtual Simulation. "Enlightenment," after this key change would refer to awakening *to* the (base) reality of actuality *from* the "dream" of virtual reality and participation in a Simulation.

112

Finally, a last, quite significant way, in which Virtual Simulation differs from Actual Simulation is that: In Actual Simulation we cannot have an actual awareness of the hypervisor – we cannot have an actual experience of what is generating the Simulation as that which is generating the Simulation; however, in Virtual Simulation, we can have an actual experience of the hypervisor that is generating the virtual reality of the Simulation. In Virtual Simulation, there is experiential access to base reality.

§4.1 How?

To ask, then, "How" a Virtual Simulation is possible, philosophically, is to focus on the difference between the levels of "reality" distinguished by the be-ing of the different types, e.g., the Virtual in contrast to the Actual. At the universal level of resolution, this question would seem to point to the – for all we know – innate process of thematizing experience. That is to say, the hypervisor of the universal level of resolution may be the natural process by way of which we make meaning. The hypervisor as the process of meaning-making regarding the *Umwelt, Mitwelt, Selbstwelt,* and *Eigenwelt* means all meaning-making be-ings are inserted into the Simulation by way of this meaning-making guiding *Welt*-matrix.

Further, we ourselves may function as hypervisors. Consider the Marxist-informed idea that as modes of production advance technologically, so too the Simulation changes. Thus, we can begin to see a difference between the Simulation and the current manner in which it expresses itself. Likewise, it is a common practice to characterize such technological evolution in economic and moral terms. In other words, the virtual reality of the Simulation itself may be understood as constituted by participation in an economy, by the power of the economy to shape the actuality in which the Simulation is rooted, and the power of the modes of production and the economy to influence the meaning-making of citizens and consumers. Notice, this latter list rephrases Baudrillard's conditions for the possibility of a Simulation, noted above.

Hence, the "How?" regarding Virtual Simulation reveals itself to be structured in the following way. First, the Simulation could be completely dependent on the technological advancement of modes of production. This would be like invoking a kind of "Blind Watchmaker" hypothesis, as if to say: Though the hypervisor may be innate to all our experiencing and meaning-making by being a part of what we *actually* are, the capacities (or the parameters of the capacities) of the hypervisor may be governed by the current state of *actual* modes of production.[26] Second, participation in the Simulation could be responsible for sustaining and developing the virtual reality of the Simulation. This may, or may not, be followed by the Simulation's reciprocal investment in its own development. Lastly, it could be a (conscious) choice in regard to meaning-making. Further, this structure of the hypervisor-Simulation relation could be thought of as depending on "attachment" to the virtual reality of the Simulation.

Token system, design of physical surrounding, and influence regarding the construction of the narrative of reality – with various incentives across each of those – seem to constitute the ontology of the hypervisor-Simulation relation in Virtual Simulation (at all levels of resolution).

§4.2 When?

To ask the question "When?" regarding Virtual Simulation is to ask the question of how the experience of Virtual time relates to the Actual time of base reality. This could be as straightforward as time understood by radioactive decay and time understood as the history of the Simulation. Of course, "history of the Simulation," in this case, would include the reciprocal influence of the Simulation's ability to develop itself to a point of seeing deeper into itself. Lastly, the question of "When?" regarding Virtual

---

[26] Notice that Virtual modes of production are Actual modes of production insofar as they actually function to produce. This may be how Virtual reality combines with Actual reality (a virtual/actual articulation of the mind/body problem). The way to resolve this puzzle will emerge below.

Simulation may be completely neutralized by anchoring the time of Virtual reality to Actual reality or by making time completely relative to the Simulation. What this last option means is that there may be no way of affixing a kind of absolute time to base reality or the Simulation. In fact, it may not even make sense to say that base reality is older than the Simulation, if it turns out that (meaning-making in terms of) directional time is merely an aspect of the Simulation.

§4.3 Constraints

Even though it may not make sense to say that base reality is older than the Simulation, it should, definitionally, make sense to say that the Simulation depends on base reality. This is reminiscent of Morpheus' speech to Neo during the "Lady in Red" scene of the first *Matrix* film. On the one hand, examining constraints regarding Virtual Simulation points directly to the relation between Virtual and Actual reality, and, specifically, to the capacities of the hypervisor. On the other hand, constraints may refer to: the extent to which we are constrained from "waking up" in the Simulation.

§4.4 Transcendence

Because we are discussing the universal level of resolution, the ability to "wake up" in the Simulation may be understood in terms of a universal aspect such as meaning-making itself or simply some capacity to resist thematization that originates externally. In other words, just like constraints, if we are to remain consistent with the logic of the universal level of resolution, then we need to say that *the capacity* for liberation is not anomalous. Perhaps some involuntary process of liberation is at work, in addition to voluntary processes, and its process of selection is anomaly-driven.

§5 Virtual Simulation: Social Level of Resolution

Recall the idea mentioned in the introduction to §4 above: Society as a Simulation. There is clearly something Hegelian at work here. On the one hand, if the Simulation were represented as a Chess gameboard, there would only be so many squares, despite the presence of so many possible squares, to which one could move next. On the other hand, imagine that movement is a requirement of existence. Then, movement from one square to another is governed by the forms of possible moves, and the limits regarding possible moves from the new position to which one is moved.

At the same time, we need not understand the development of the virtual reality of the Simulation at the social level of resolution as involuntary or completely beyond our control. Along this way of characterizing Simulation at the social level of resolution, here is where notions of control and technological slavery enter the discussion. Further, typically, these notions are thought of as grounded in modes of production, such as Capitalism, or forms of government, such that lead to overt control or, in the case of the former, the twofold influence of identity-as-consumer and manufactured-desire.

This is the context in which we are reminded of Post-Humanism and Trans-Humanism. When technology lifts us *out of* our earthly limits *into* what does it place us? Does it place us into a virtual reality? If so, according to the point of view of the social level of resolution, this is insertion into a Simulation. This is why Postmodern thinkers like Lyotard and Baudrillard could apply "gaming" metaphors to characterize such a Virtual kind of reality. In the most direct terms, to think of oneself in worldly and historical terms is to occupy a Virtual horizon of meaning as the play-ground of the natural meaning-making process.

§5.1 How?

How, then, is Virtual Simulation at the social level of resolution possible? One possibility is in terms of the oscillation between higher and lower worlds. In other words, it is possible to imagine an object or an event that has not yet come into existence or manifested. Of course, we can also use what we have imagined to guide us as we bring the object into existence or manifest (some version of) the events imagined in our fantasies. When the existence of those regulative imaginings or regulative visions depends on technology, then reality may be thought of as shaped and influenced by truly virtual sources.

This virtualization shows that desire can be manufactured and it is "How" a process of desire can become "hijacked." In existential language, we could say that authentic existence means the *Eigen-Welt* is sustained as primary regulator/governor despite activity in the *Um-Welt*, *Mit-Welt*, and *Selbst-Welt*. Thus, to be inserted into, or find oneself always already involved in, a token system, to recognize the manner in which the limits of the physical dimension constrain us, and to recognize that, in many significant ways, "The limits of my language mean the limits of my world" (Wittgenstein, 1922: 5.6) is to recognize oneself as participating in a partially-virtual reality. To the extent that the Virtual part of that partially-virtual reality becomes a primary regulator/governor, then one may be living in a Simulation.

Baudrillard's celebrated way of stating this is:
> Whoever fakes an illness can simply stay in bed and make everyone believe he is ill. Whoever *simulates* an illness produces in himself some of the symptoms.'
> Therefore, pretending... leaves the principle of reality intact: the difference is always clear, it is simply masked, whereas *Simulation* threatens the difference between the 'true' and the 'false,' the 'real' and the 'imaginary.' (2017: 3).

In this way, to be inserted into a Simulation relies on kind of "pretending." And, that insight indicates both the Simulations constraints and the path of the individual to "unplug," the path of the individual to transcend a Virtual Simulation at the social level.

When we ask about the role of economics in the construction and sustenance of the Simulation, we find Capital's interest in the power of advertising. Thus, the other part of "How?" is monetization through advertising, everyone now speaks the language of "like and subscribe." These historical changes brought about by changes in how an economy is understood and managed illustrate the reciprocal shaping of host and parasite, of how a Simulation is able to become anchored in a soul and how the drive of the individual feeds the beast that pretends them both in a Simulation. Here is the passage from Baudrillard:

> Today what we are experiencing is the absorption of all virtual modes of expression into that of advertising. All original cultural forms, all determined languages are absorbed in advertising because it has no depth, it is instantaneous and instantaneously forgotten. *Triumph of superficial form, of the smallest common denominator of all signification* [emphasis added], degree zero of meaning... (2017: 87).

Of course, this triumph could not have occurred without technology mediating our experiences in the *Um-Welt* and *Mit-Welt*. Moreover, such alterations in the *Um-Welt* and *Mit-Welt* have led to changes in the *Selbst-Welt*.

Baudrillard can be read as commenting on this insight in the following passage:

> At the hegemonic stage of technology, of world power, human beings have lost their freedom, but they have also lost their imagination. They have been made unemployed in a way that goes far beyond work: it is a mental and existential unemployment...

These technical layoffs suggest the opposite of what the term usually means: the machines are not defective; they are so efficient that there is nothing left to do with one's life, even its reproduction has become automatic. (2010: 79-80).

It is as if humans can no longer imagine a life outside of the one's suggested by Capital's Virtual social Simulation.

It is worth considering a couple passages out of Deleuze's writings in regard to these same topics. Hearkening back to the "description of the Simulation as evidenced by historical change" ideas noted above, Deleuze spoke of the transition from "societies of sovereignty" to "disciplinary societies" to "societies of control."

"Control" is the name Burroughs proposes as a term for the new monster, one that Foucault recognizes as our immediate future. Paul Virilio also is continually analyzing the ultrarapid forms of free-floating control that replaced the old disciplines operating in the time frame of a closed system. (1992: 4).

Whereas disciplinary societies may be understood as anchoring Simulation more in the idea of physical manipulation of the environment, that is, the *Um-Welt*, the current Simulation utilizes "free-floating control." The ability to remove an individual's access to their own money by way of "electronically freezing their accounts." Or, consistent surveillance as an aspect of "free-floating control," for example, through one's smartphone, vehicle navigation system, and public video cameras.

Deleuze's comments regarding the difference between societies of control and disciplinary societies provides helpful illumination here. "Man is no longer man enclosed, but man in debt." (1992: 6). For, "The operation of markets is now the instrument of social control... Control is short-term and of rapid rates of turnover, but also continuous and without limit" (Ibid). And,

Perhaps it is money that expresses the distinction between the two societies best, since discipline always referred back to minted money that locks gold in as numerical standard, while control relates to floating rates of exchange, modulated according to a rate established by a set of standard currencies. (1992: 5; cf. Mullins, 2009).

Deleuze seemed to understand technological evolution and economic development as tightly coupled. His thoughts on this are worth quoting at length:

> The old societies of sovereignty made use of simple machines – levers, pulleys, clocks; but the recent disciplinary societies equipped themselves with machines involving energy... the societies of control operate with machines of a third type, computers... This technological evolution must be, even more profoundly, a mutation of capitalism, an already well-known or familiar mutation that can be summed up as follows: nineteenth-century capitalism is a capitalism of concentration, for production and for property. [Yet, in societies of control it is] no longer a capitalism for production but for the product, which is to say, for being sold or marketed [cf. Baudrillard regarding advertising]. Thus, it is essentially dispersive, and the factory has given way to the corporation. (Ibid: 6; cf. Althusser, 2014).

To clarify,

> Foucault has brilliantly analyzed the ideal project of [the disciplinary societies'] environments of enclosure, particularly visible within the factory: to concentrate; to distribute in space; to order in time; to compose a productive force within the dimension of space-time whose effect will be greater than the sum of its component forces. (Ibid: 3).

When we consider the kinds of jobs that exist in society and ask why they exist, it becomes possible to see the way that technological and economic development shape the world. That the world can be shaped in such a way may be considered evidence of a Virtual Simulation at the social level of resolution. Hence, the above discussed ways answer "How?" such a Simulation may constitute a kind of virtual reality shaping (and possibly "controlling") humans.

§5.2 When?

The "When?" question may be understood, then, in one of two ways. First, it may be asking in regard to where in social development our current version of the Matrix, the current version of the Simulation, is located. This refers, for example, to the progression from "societies of sovereignty" to "disciplinary societies" to "societies of control." Second, it may be asking in regard to the revelatory moment when the Simulation reveals itself, that is, when changing from one system to another, like the experience of *déjà vu* in *The Matrix* films. According to Baudrillard,

> Interface and performance: the two leitmotifs of today. In performance, all forms of expression are combined... This vertical and horizontal, aesthetic and commercial diversification is now part of the work... A (non-) event like *The Matrix* serves as a perfect example: it is the very model of a global installation, of a total world event. Not only the film, which is only an excuse to some extent, but the spin-off products, the simultaneous projection at all points of the globe and millions of spectators themselves who are inextricably part of it. We are all, from a global and interactive point of view, actors in this total world event. (2005: 94).

It is as if the very possibility of globalization betrays that the "world" was always already a Simulation. And, recalling his earlier comment, the machines have become so efficient that there's simply nothing left for humans to do.

§5.3 Constraints

In Section 5 of this chapter, we have been discussing Virtual Simulation at the social level of resolution. We identified three elements by way of which one can be plugged-into a Simulation. Further, we mentioned that these elements indicate both constraints and points of potential transcendence. For, it would make sense to say that if those are the elements by which a Simulation is capable of "linking" to a sentient being, then, evidently, Simulations are constrained in, at least, those ways. That is to say, if one could resist one of the elements, then that individual may be able to disrupt their relation to the dream from which they can't seem to wake.

§5.4 Transcendence

On the one hand, we need not conceive of the relation between sentient beings and Simulations Romantically. It may be possible that Simulations are responsible for all discursive meaning, all discursivizing of reality. Moreover, "discursiving of reality" may be understood as being a kind of virtualization. On the other hand, it still seems to be true that the constraints of the Simulation are points at which the Simulation may be overcome. The question is whether the Simulation can be used for some ultimate good or if the system of control cannot, itself, be controlled.

Very simply, the idea here may be characterized in the following way. In the spirit of Deleuze and Baudrillard above, we may say, "Could capitalism be put to some ultimately good end?" It seems they would respond by pointing out that the mere participation in the development of the system of control leads to its ever-increasing capacity to control. In other words, *it is not possible to enhance the Simulation for the sake of liberation from the Simulation.* Of course, it may be objected here, "Why would anyone ever want to be liberated from the Simulation?" And, Deleuze and Baudrillard could respond without even invoking ideas such as pollution and extinction; they could merely point to any number of soteriological formulas to be found in various ethical systems. Even without invoking an *Eigen-Welt*, simply being alienated from one's own *Actual* sentience could function as justification to want to transcend a Virtual Simulation.

§6 Virtual Simulation: Individual Level of Resolution

I'd like to begin this section by sharing two ideas, upfront, as it were: The first we could call the "skeptic's bubble." My favorite example of the skeptic's bubble, I call, "the headphones example." (cf. Scalambrino, 2016). There have been times (particularly when writing books) that I would listen to music on headphones. I would often find something upbeat that I could bracket out of my conscious experience. This would have an uplifting effect on my spirit and help me to sit and type for days, seemingly, without end. One day, when typing in a room occupied by other people, I took off my headphones, and I recognized that what I was experiencing wasn't what the others in the same environment were experiencing. For a discussion of how that relates to ethics see my *Introduction to Ethics* textbook; however, for our purposes here, I'll just say such a *bubble* illustrates how the virtual reality of a Virtual Simulation may be experienced at the individual level of resolution.

The second idea, then, is technological mediation. There is a reason that technology is consistently associated with the Wands suit of the Tarot. It is as if technology can be wielded like a magic wand. On the one hand, to the extent that Simulation theory adheres to an idea of a base reality, then there will always be a ground that is naturally more primordial than a Simulation. This is why humans are often depicted as "plugged into" a Simulation; rather than simply a part of the Simulation. On the other hand, just as headphones are an example of technology, I think the use of technology to mediate experience enhances what otherwise may be a kind of *natural* "bubbling" for humans. Technological mediation not only makes it easier to witness bubbling regarding ourselves and others; it also intensifies the bubble, and, thereby, may be understood as intensifying one's participation in a Simulation.

In a peculiar way, though the Simulation repeatedly tells you who and what you are, there is a natural harmony with one's primordial be-ing in that we feel alienated from a self without identity. That is to say, if the Simulation is responsible for assigning us an identity, then in *its terms* it would be *"non-*identity" that refers to our true primordial self. Thus, we can also become increasingly alienated the "deeper" into a Simulation we go. Stated in existentialist terms, it is alienation *into* the world (*Welt*). *Da-Sein* as Be-ing-in-the-World, is alienated from itself as individuated Be-ing. Specifically, Simulation regarding the *Mit-Welt* and *Selbst-Welt* seem more prominent in the context of the more social aspects of media, that is, technological mediation. Yet, the reality of the *Um-Welt*, as physical surrounding environment, certainly can be questioned in light of the power of technological mediation to change the actual physicality of "the World."

Now that we are primed by those two ideas, we can state the meaning of Virtual Simulation at the individual level of resolution with three thoughts: First, it is the idea that your actual self is in base reality and that your social identity is a kind of virtualization. Notice the contrast between individual and social in the previous sentence. It makes sense that at the individual level of resolution the individual distinguishes itself from every other individual. Second, the idea here is that every Actual individual can potentially be unplugged from the Simulation, because (definitionally even) the reality of the Simulation is merely Virtual. Hence, the individual level of Virtual Simulation is essentially distinct from all of the levels of resolution belonging to Mental Simulation. Third, even if the Simulation can alter the *Um-Welt*, there is an aspect of the *Um-Welt* that is ontologically different from the Simulation; And, that is because that aspect is Actual, and the Simulation is Virtual. This is another important aspect to keep in mind because it differentiates the individual level of resolution regarding Virtual Simulation from all of the levels of resolution belonging to Mental Simulation.

§6.1 How?

To ask, then, "How" a Virtual Simulation at the individual level is possible is, first and foremost, to ask: "How is it possible that only some individuals are participating in a Simulation?" Or, its inverse, "How is it possible that some individuals are not participating in a Simulation?" I didn't initially foresee that I would be emphasizing the following example from the first *Matrix* film to characterize the difference between Virtual Simulation at the individual level of resolution and Mental Simulation in general. However, as can be seen by the above question, the following aspect of *The Matrix* directly addresses the essence of the distinction.

The example comes from the first "lady in red" scene. There, Morpheus tells Neo anyone not unplugged is potentially an agent of the Matrix. One, this sounds like agency or will of the Matrix, as opposed to one's own will. Two, considering Morpheus' distinction analogically with the existential context, in general, and inauthenticity, in particular, provides additional illumination regarding constraints and transcendence at both the Virtual individual level of resolution and Mental Simulation in general, that is, all levels of resolution regarding Mental Simulation. Three, Morpheus' distinction illuminates a distinction between entities who can be separated from the Matrix and entities who cannot.

So, let's focus on this third idea for our discussion, here, and, then, return to it at the beginning of the Mental Simulation chapter. In regard to Virtual Simulation, then, Virtual Simulation at the individual level of resolution seems to *necessarily* hold that all individuals can potentially be unplugged. In fact, this insight pertains to both the ontological and the soteriological (constraints and transcendence) dimensions of Virtual Simulation. This is because base reality is so clearly differentiated from virtual reality in Virtual Simulation.

Interestingly, whereas Morpheus' distinction is a *necessary* component of the ontological structure of Virtual Simulation, it is *ambiguous* regarding the ontological structure of Actual Simulation. And, how Mental Simulation relates to Morpheus' distinction is a little more complicated. I will discuss this prior to Chapter 3, §4.

Hence, the "How?" question regarding Virtual Simulation at the individual level must allow for the possibility that all Actual individuals (located in base reality and) participating in the Virtual Simulation must be able to "unplug" from (i.e., transcend the) Simulation. Thus, we can see a spectrum along which a person's will may be more or less "hijacked" (perhaps I should say, "hacked"?) by the Simulation. And, though all of the individuals have the potential to unplug from the Virtual reality of the Simulation, at the extreme end of the spectrum, perhaps an individual could be too absorbed into the Matrix to ultimately be able to successfully "unplug."

§6.2 When?

The "When?" question at the individual level of resolution, since in Virtual Simulation there is necessarily a base reality, may be understood as the temporal characterization of the "How?" spectrum just noted above. This may be understood differently depending upon which end of the spectrum one takes as a point of view. For example, on the one hand, from the point of view of base reality, "When?" may refer to the level of one's development toward "unplugging." This is, of course, intimately connected with constraints and transcendence. This is the case, since the extent to which one is "absorbed" into the agency of the Simulation functions as a constraint toward "unplugging" from the Simulation, and the extent to which one has developed toward "unplugging" indicates one's transcendence.

Thus, on the other hand, from the point of view of having become an agent of the Simulation, the "When?" question would be determined by the Simulation's temporal ordering of virtual reality. This is not simply the suggestion that the year is currently 2022; rather, it would also include the manner in which the Simulation determines the meaning of time for all the actual individuals plugged into it. Thus, "a gap year," "date night," and holidays driven by, for example, Capitalism are all examples of how simple memes (aka thought contagions) could ripple through a Virtual Simulation influencing how the time existing in base reality is understood.

§6.3 Constraints

It is interesting to recognize the manner in which the necessary aspect of the ontology of Virtual Simulation at the individual level determines the constraints and transcendence characteristics of its soteriology. Thus, we have already discussed the manner in which the distinction between the Actual individual in base reality who is plugged into the virtual reality of the Virtual Simulation constrains the manner in which the Virtual Simulation and the individual are related.

§6.4 Transcendence

The same thing that was just said regarding constraints may, of course, be said of transcendence regarding Virtual Simulation at the individual level. Of all of the Simulation types and levels of resolution discussed, then, Virtual Simulation at the individual level of resolution seems to be the most intuitive and least ambiguous portion of Simulation theory. In short, to state it again, the necessary distinction between *Actual* base reality and the *Virtual* reality characterizing the ontology of Virtual Simulation also determines its soteriology. That is to say, salvation from the Simulation necessarily means transcendence to the actuality of base reality.

Chapter 3: Mental Simulation

Dr. Pittman

The assertion by Anil Seth[27] that *reality is a hallucination* is a good illustration of how we define the third type of Simulation. For my part, I am interested in fleshing out the Mental substrate, virtualization architecture, and associated computational components needed to render such hallucinations. I am curious to see how far we can push the Mental Simulation idea without running into an argument concerning a bad interpretation of computational theory of mind[28].

Mental Simulation turns our prior Set Theory descriptions on their heads because of the strange ability for the Mental to imagine or create elements not in the parent or superset. Better said, from the outside it appears as if the mind can create things- words, sounds, smells, and objects- not otherwise present. Yet, this is an illusion woven by deft and silent hands.

If we continue in the language of *The Matrix* films, the ability for humans to break natural law within the Simulation aptly illustrates Mental Simulation. Surely humans cannot fly, for instance. A person cannot leap *into* another person, right? If we were still operating in the context of Actual or Virtual Simulation, I would agree those things are impossible. However, Mental Simulation presents a reality unlimited, unbound by convention.

---

[27] https://ed.ted.com/lessons/your-brain-hallucinates-your-conscious-reality-anil-seth

[28] Computational theory mind holds that the mind is a computational system. The *bad interpretation* I mention here is in reference to the popular take on the idea which is minds are computers. We must remember all computers are computational systems but not all computational systems are computers. Computers, better defined, are information processing systems.

I suggest it is not our understanding of physics that is wrong as much as the question is operating at an incompatible layer of abstraction. For comparison: can things fly? Maybe. It depends. We can remove the ambiguity by reframing *things* as some *animals*.

Mental Simulation is a third-order nested subset. We can state that Mental Simulation is the set of positive integers nested within the total set of integers which itself is a subset of the real numbers. This is the continuation of our numbers example for reference.

Uniquely, we can also observe additional nesting in isolating the odd positive integers from the positive integers and so forth. Such progressive nesting is possible because of the properties of numbers (i.e., the arithmetic in a traditional sense). Likewise, as the rest of this chapter demonstrates, Mental Simulation is capable of powerful nesting procedures.

Another powerful aspect of Mental Simulation is its ability to invert the relation between the Simulation and the source of the Simulation. The relation between Machine, Simulation, and Simulation of Simulations, is the epitome of a many-to-many relation. Further, as much as we are now firmly in the realm of Type 2 virtualization hypervisors, we are also in a new place. The new place is where a virtualized Simulation substrate can instantiated additional hypervisors of distinct types. The ramifications will be evident throughout the Universal, Social, and Individual level of resolutions.

§1 Mental Simulation: Universal Level of Resolution

The Universal level of Simulation defines the set of all things simulated. The set in this context includes things at once defined and definable by the mind. As peculiar as this may seem, I think the bounding of the set makes sense. We are establishing what the Mental universe consists of maximally and building towards the computational essence of the Mental-Universal substrate.

Mental-Universal Simulation exists decoupled from the first-order Simulation (Actual) and the second-order Simulation (Virtual). Those Simulations presented as base reality and a Virtual reality instantiated of base reality. Mental Simulation at the Universal level of resolution is the Simulation of a *consciousness*. This comes across as admittedly non-computational. Nevertheless, I suspect the computational nature of Mental-Universal Simulation is evident in the artifacts of the Simulation.

§1.1 How?

The critical departure from the Actual and Virtual types of Simulation rests with the Mental Simulation behaving as both a layer of Simulation and a loading construct for nested Simulation. Hints of how this form of Simulation is instantiated came from Virtual-Individual. The differentiation is the change in substrate architecture. Notwithstanding such architecture transformation, I cannot overstate how materially different virtualization and input-output filtering could be as well.

We should consider the substrate for this type and resolution of Simulation to be psychological. I am not implying the substrate possesses a psychology to be clear. Rather, the substrate is the effect of a Mental cause. Along these lines, the Mental is a Simulation itself and the Mental-Universal is a nested Simulation therein. This is not unlike the Virtual-Individual Simulation in terms of logical architecture. It also is not identical of course and there is where we should train our focus.

One way to situate our focus is to imagine that an Actual Simulation at Universal level of resolution is a classic top-down construction. Comparatively, the Mental Simulation is a classic bottom-up. The Mental Simulation constructs the universe rather than the universe constructing the Mental. We get even more divergent substrate architecture when we realize the Simulation can manifest an unlimited number of nested Mental-Universal substrates itself.

Geometrically, we can call to mind two-dimensional. The dimensionality of Mental Simulation can appear zero-dimensional (Actual Simulation) or one-dimensional (Virtual Simulation). Further, the extra possible dimension is the result of Mental Simulation having the capacity to nest additional sub-Simulations. The geometry can grow vertically in addition to laterally. The effect is a hyper connected mesh framework of Mental-Universal Simulations.

The oddness of the Mental-Universal Simulation is not over. I want to point out that the substrate need not be common across all Simulations or even across all sub-Simulations stemming from a parent Mental Simulation. Odder still is the idea that a sub-substrate does not have to be computational. The root Mental Simulation can superimpose the nature of computation onto noncomputational objects. This extends to Selection Functions as well because the Mental Simulation embeds the functions in the substrate.

Mental-Universal Simulation does introduce a disproportionate amount of complexity. Honestly, the complexity is not going away as we move through the rest of this work. However, we can tease apart the complexity and come to understand it if we take care in examining how virtualization manifests this type of Simulation.

I want to define a phrase that has slipped into our Simulation lexicon: *virtualization stack*. I intend *stack* to mean something more than just a collection of technologies. A stack is a symbiotic arrangement of technologies. Stacks are ecosystems whereby the whole combines a singular entity. Not only does stack better represent how the compute resources align to power the Simulation but having a single term to represent the underlying complexity of the virtualization will maintain clarity for us.

The difference between virtualization in the Mental and the Virtual Simulations is subtle but meaningful. The Mental type is a Simulation (the mind as an innermost universe) within a Simulation (the body as a middle universe) which is itself nested in a Simulation (the universe). This sequence is a virtualization stack. The substrate is not the same which is why the stack is not identical to the Virtual-Individual virtualization.

Mental Simulation at the Universal level of resolution corresponds to a Type 2 virtualization kernel. The Machine physical substrate decouples entirely from the Simulation. By consequence, the hypervisor simulates what *hardware* is necessary to instantiate the Simulation. All compute resources within the Simulation appear physical though. Visually this looks like an inverted pyramid. Everything simulated is dependent upon a single virtualization stack bottleneck.

I think input and output filtering occurs in the Universal level of resolution of Mental Simulation. Moreover, because of the substrate and virtualization architecture, there are multiple levels of filters stacked up in a form of Mental titration. Whether such input is towards the origin Mental substrate, or its derivative Mental states, is an important distinction.

Unlike with the Actual and Virtual types, output at the Individual level of resolution can feedback into itself as input to the Simulation Function. We can take the base reality universe as input to the first tier in the virtualization stack. This pairs output-input all the way up into the Mental Simulation. The flow of input leads me to think the virtualization stack places filters in derivative Mental states.

§1.2 What?

The manifestation of a universe in thought is an effective way to conceptualize Mental-Universal Simulation. This represents a substantive departure from the Actual and Virtual types. Such departure is related to the mechanisms of Mental Simulation. The departure is also related to the innards of the Simulation. Gone is the direct input of a base reality element and its rendering in the Simulation. Instead, Simulation here is a Mental construction based on general base reality abstractions.

Variance between Mental Simulations in this level of resolution would be substantial enough such that no two instantiations would be identical. The same Simulation may not be consistent within its own runtime even. This degree of variance is related to the massive change in substrate. A Type 2 hypervisor may not seem that different than a Type 1.5, but it is different. I do not think this is the whole story though.

I want to revisit the keys on the table example. We can reframe the question slightly. What if the keys were on a different side of the table? I cannot imagine easily dismissing such an occurrence easily unless it was a one-off exception. The drastic repositioning of keys on a table would not be an exception in a Mental Simulation though. I take this as an attribute of frequency to the running Simulation variance. We can frame this as degree of computational forgetfulness.

Mental Simulation at the level of Universal resolution strikes me as being organic. The term *organic* might be a strange choice here. It is but I don't know how else to depict how a Mental substrate exhibits repetition and change. Organic does not mean static of course. Rather, organic implies a natural rate of change. The variance inherent to Mental Simulation hinted at this property.

Let me state repetition and change in Mental-Universal Simulation may not consistently manifest to an internal observer. The Programmer may not be responsible for repetition and change. These might be emergent from the Mental substrate itself. There is no longer a discrete separation between Simulation backdrop and active foreground.

Such organicism is programmable. I think the programming would need to be at a level of fundamental building blocks which include change and repetition paradigms[29]. The Mental hypervisor would extrapolate these constructs from fundamental element into Simulation elements.

A Mental-Universal Simulation may have multiple levels of fidelity. The Mental Simulation must have a powerful capacity for generating what it is supposed to represent. This is more critical than Actual and Virtual Simulations because of the way hypervisors can nest. Without any doubt a Mental Simulation perceiving the Universal would be a complex picture. The foreground would have tremendous fidelity while the middle and background would progressively have less. At the same time, things not within an active Mental field of view would have diminished fidelity.

A flashlight with multiple beams of light illustrates fidelity in this context. The flashlight produces these beams as nested, concentric circles. The innermost circle has the most power allocated to it and thus shines the brightest. Moving outward, each beam is less bright. The outer beams reveal less out of the darkness.

The Mental-Universal is a modal instantiation in terms of resolution. The latest Matrix (Matrix Resurrections) film employs this concept to illustrate how a Simulation can be instantiated within a Simulation. The modal maintains a barrier between the two. The resolution is not different between sides of the barrier. The modal provides a bounding circumference or focus though. What is *inside* the modal has resolution but is not the resolution.

---

[29] The field of Artificial Life works to solve problems by mimicking natural life through the programming of fundamental building blocks such as DNA. For those curious, this might be a place to begin exploring the computational aspects of nonbiological organic objects.

A practical example of the modal resolution is a modern website application. The modal window containing the login or contact form loads *over top of* the main site. There is no difference in rendered resolution between the two windows. There is a resolution focal difference driven by the bounding of what is modal versus what is not modal.

On the contrary, the error rate and accuracy within the modal could be materially different than the enveloping Mental Simulation. Neither are zero, however. I can say *nonzero* with confidence because of the rate of errors is no less than Virtual-Universal. Furthermore, the artifact trend has consistently been increases in Simulation complexity yield rises in error rates.

The Mental-Universal has a hidden error multiplier embedded in the hypervisor-substrate. If it were just the core Mental substrate, we might have a clear idea of how much the Simulation encounters error. The hidden multiplier is there is not just one Mental substrate. The substrate has the capability to nest hypervisors. Thus, the meaningful fidelity measure is accuracy. The area to look at the Simulation accuracy would be on the modal border.

The modal border is also where interaction at the Universal level of resolution exists. I think the sensitivity aspect of Simulation fidelity tracks alongside error and accuracy. The modal border is the sensitivity artifact and the evidence of Mental-Universal capability for interaction. What becomes difficult now is how a Programmer can observe the precision of the Simulation. I think the answer is the Programmer in base reality cannot interact with the core Mental substrate let alone any nested substrates downstream from there. However, the Programmer could inject the fundamental components for the construction of a virtualized Programmer embodied in the nested hypervisor.

§1.3 When?

Time in Mental Simulation at the Universal level of resolution progresses at the same tick rate as the hypervisor. Nested hypervisors interlink with the lower order hypervisor. The lower order hypervisor links to the origin Mental substrate. All of which is soft linked at best to the base reality Machine clock. I use the term *soft-linked* because of how the Mental instantiates Simulation through a series of loosely coupled artifacts. The interlinked series of tick rates are the time measurement.

I think my use of the term series might imply something I don't intend. To explain, the Mental-Universal *when* architecture is not so much a linear chain as it is concentric rings. Time is a singular, constant artifact in this case, but it is not additive. Each nested ring defines its own Mental *when* artifacts based on yet independent from the layer of *when* above and below. Ripples in a pond comes to mind as an illustration.

I do think time is consistent across the Mental-Universal Simulations. This is despite potentially having a multitude of hypervisors and thus a multitude of Simulations running concurrently. I think this is true because *when* is a Universal Mental construction with a seed input from the instantiating hypervisor. The instantiated hypervisor pins *when* using the seed input. While this does not prevent a clock from drifting from its origin, it does guarantee a known good origin reference. The reference is necessary for when the Simulation spawns a nested hypervisor onto a child process thread adjacent to the Mental-Simulation thread. This is multi-threaded concurrency with a linear arrangement of the threads.

§1.4 Constraints

Simulation cannot exceed the constraints imposed through base reality natural law. Without a doubt, natural law from base reality affects the structural makeup of Mental-Universal Simulation. However, we are dealing with an entirely different substrate now. Specifically, the Mental is non-physical. Thus, Mental-Universal Simulation may bring about more of the same constraints but in unique and strange implementations.

To the point, I think the substrate drives the constraints appearing from base reality natural law and applies them to Mental Simulation at the Universal level of resolution. This contrasts with the virtualization hypervisor as in Virtual-Universal or the Machine as in Actual-Universal. I say this because the Mental has the capability to rearrange, to modify how constraints manifest since it is generating the Simulation directly.

Furthermore, given we also have the ability for nesting of substrates in this architecture, I wonder how constraint inheritance functions. It might be possible for some constraints to simply passthrough to a nested substrate. Others may not passthrough. The substrate's nature could have the constraints baked into the instantiation process. Overall, I suspect we still need to consider the same set of constraints given the Mental idea of a Universal seems to be at least consistent with the Actual universe.

Without a doubt, compute power, energy, and storage constrain the Mental-Universal Simulation differently than Actual or Virtual. The implementation of a Mental-Universal Simulation conforms to the same constraints as we defined in the Actual-Universal discussion. The implementation is different, however.

Let's discuss compute power for example. Base reality natural law constrains compute power. Within the constraint, we can assume the Machine is producing as much compute power as *naturally* possible. Thus, as we have seen thus far, the secret of any Simulation is not to generate more compute power but to use available compute more effectively. Effective in the Mental Simulation type would manifest as less power directed towards the base reality Machine, more power directed to the Mental substrate. Energy would simply follow the architecture as such defines compute power.

With storage, each instantiated Type 2 hypervisor will require its own storage component. Each of these hypervisors, whether there are multiple lateral Simulations or multiple nested Simulations, must be able to persistent certain artifacts. At the same time, we are dealing with a Universal level of resolution and therefore what is persisted is at least a unified data fabric. I foresee a tradeoff between potential for storage sprawl and complexity in signaling and communications.

We think of Actual Simulation signaling and communication as straight line between base reality and its simulated analogue. Virtual is a hub-and-spoke. The next evolution is for Mental Simulation signal and communication to adopt a star-mesh topology (Fig. 7).

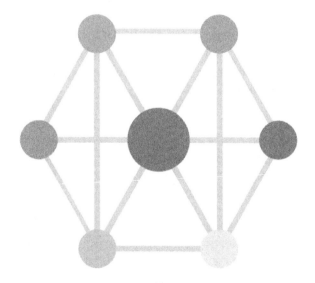

Fig. 7: The logical Mental Simulation topology

The illustration is important for discussing the potential signaling and communication constraints because it visually demonstrates the advantages of a star-mesh architecture while also revealing its areas of weakness. With the topology in mind, I think the largest advantage compared to other types is the interconnectedness of *everything*. Coincidentally and oddly enough, the largest disadvantage is the same interconnectedness.

Think back to the example of T-join pipe junctions as we left off in the Virtual-Individual Simulation. We ought to see how interconnectedness gives us robustness and resilience but brings forth increasing amounts of complexity. The notion of robustness and resilience means we have more flexibility on how signaling-communications flow. The Simulation has fewer single points of failure overall. As a result, we need more and more architecture dedicated to maintaining and overseeing the signaling and communications for things like loss, jitter, and congestion. Ideally, we want to encapsulate the signaling-communications junctions within the scope of discrete Mental-Universal Simulations. The effect is that of a snow globe.

Let a snow globe stand for a Mental-Universal Simulation. We have a notable example of interoperability when move the snow globe across shelves. Interoperability would also be swapping bases holding the snow globe. Mental-Universal is interoperable across any computational substrate. Nested Simulations inside the Mental-Universal are interoperable with any such super-ordinate virtualized substrate. The physical Machine infrastructure does not maintain a tight coupling with what the substrate instantiates as Simulation.

The Mental-Universal Simulation is an extensible Simulation because of the interoperability. The substrate can inject changes or updates to the Simulation infrastructure while the Simulation is running. Changes and updates would flow from upstream, from base reality up through the physical Machine substrate into the Type 2 hypervisor.

Put simply, we can check integrity against the root Mental substrate and its first order instantiated Simulation but nothing more. A nested Simulation, or interactions therein, would implement integrity checking within those boundaries. Likewise, integrity information would not be available across Simulations. Otherwise, the computational mechanisms for checking integrity are identical to previous Simulation types and resolutions.

§2 Mental Simulation: Social Level of Resolution

Mental-Social Simulation is a convergence of base reality, the Mental Simulation substrates, and a nested Mental architecture of social elements or constructs. This convergence results in a Simulation quite different than the Actual or Virtual Social versions. The Mental incarnation of Social still encapsulates society and social interaction. The underlying computational systems leading to the Simulation of those characteristics harbor a degree of difference though.

Sets best express the degree of difference. The Set Theory explanation for Mental-Social outlines the framework of how the Simulation is possible. We are dealing with a proper subset that is itself a proper subset of an upstream super set. The amount of deviation in the computational architecture allows for this Set Theory alignment. We will simplify this as we more fully describe the Mental-Social Simulation.

For now, an indicative example of Mental-Social Simulation from the source material is the concept of an NPC or non-player character[30]. More specifically, NPCs inhabit the Social level of resolution which defines the Social through programmed behaviors. The Mental then is

---

[30] Where a Player Character represents the player in avatar form, the NPC represents computer-controlled avatars. NPCs have specific programmed behaviors, following a tight script as they interact with the simulated world. NPCs also have programmed emergent behaviors and dynamic, organic interactions with the world, other NPCs, and the PC.

the non-programmed interaction emergent from the non-physical, non-virtual substrate.

§2.1 How?

Mental Simulation at the Universal level of resolution is psychological rather than physical or virtual. The Social resolution is an extension of the same. To that end, the Mental-Social Simulation is not as radically different from Mental-Universal as the latter is from the Actual and Virtual Simulation types. I suspect there are minor architectural shifts with large effects.

A significant difference is how the substrate is able to load the synthetic Social constructs. We should not lose track of the essential computational aspect of Simulation despite the oddity of a Mental Simulation type. In other words, a computational substrate is by its nature the same as any other computational substrate. Differences in instantiated objects is an effect caused by differences in the substrate.

The Mental Simulation at the Social level of resolution is a substrate (Mental) that loads the social primitives. Such primitives are a set of potential social element inputs. A nested Simulation Function uses such input to assemble the Mental-Social. As well, each nested Simulation Function also contains the selection algorithm responsible for identifying which Social elements to inject upstream into the Mental-Social Simulation.

Meanwhile, the Social level of resolution necessitates that its substrate be instantiated within the operational environment of a Mental-Universal Simulation. The result is a chain of Simulation substrates. The base reality Machine chains to a hypervisor. The hypervisor chains to Mental substrate-hypervisor. Mental substrate-hypervisor chains to Mental-Universal substrate and then finally the Social Simulation. Let's look at a simple illustration to cut through the complexity of this arrangement.

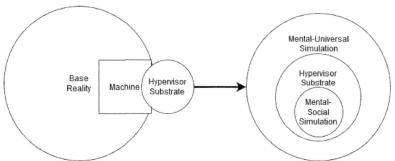

Fig. 8: The relationship between Machine, hypervisor-substrate, and nested Mental Simulation architecture

The Mental-Social substrate is robust. The substrate supports a rapid expansion in how the Simulation can be instantiated. To start, as in the Mental-Universal Simulation, the virtualization at the Social level of resolution comes from a Type 2 hypervisor. Next, we have the element level Social input coming through the physical Machine pipeline into the hypervisor.

The Virtual-Social exhibits a unified substrate and virtualization architecture though. This eliminates the differentiation between backdrop Simulation and active Simulation. I think the same architecture is present here, but it is implemented another way. The Mental-Social is a Type 2 hypervisor nested within an outer Simulation powered also by a Type 2 hypervisor. The outer hypervisor provides the equivalent of the backdrop. The nested hypervisor loads the Social in *seamless*[31] mode as a focal foreground.

I'd like to point out an example of virtualization using the Mental-Social concept is the Construct from *The Matrix* films. I perceive the Construct, as a shared virtualization into which Mental Simulations are instantiated. The shared virtualization allows Social contexts (e.g., guns,

---

[31] Seamless mode is a technique to load virtualized software on a Type 2 hypervisor without the need for interacting with a full virtualized operating system desktop environment. To be fair, the operating system is still loaded but is, in so many words, not visible.

kung-fu training, etc.) to be loaded from the fundamental base reality elements.

With the example of *The Matrix* films in mind, we might wonder how so many different guns, kung-fu trainings, and so forth the Construct can load. I contend the answer is apertures, Selection Functions, and input-output filters.

Principally, the Social level of resolution narrows the aperture. This is precisely how the aperture operated in the Actual and Virtual Simulation types as well. I suspect the difference in Mental-Social architecture places the aperture deeper into the virtualization stack. The effect is every Type 2 hypervisor contains its own aperture.

Further, each substrate contains an embedded Selection Function which executes against the input stream. Thus, the Selection Function parses specific Social elements out of the input stream and injects those elements into the Simulation output. The presence of this feature implies programmability in every substrate as each load into its nested compartment.

Finally, the Social level of resolution uses output filters as well. Here, the output filters might be necessary to upgrade or downgrade the Simulation stream fidelity. This mirrors how line conditioners stabilize power between a wall outlet and systems using the outlet.

§2.2 What?

Whereas Mental-Universal Simulation is the thought of a universe, the Mental-Social Simulation is the phenomenological interaction with society and societal constructs situated in an abstracted universe. The complexity of Simulation rises in proportion to the Mental substrate generating a universe backdrop. Society envelopes in the middle ground. Discrete social interactions constitute the Simulation proper. Such complexity means we need to give attention to variance, repetition, change, as well as fidelity of the Simulation.

Doing so allows us to differentiate this type of Simulation from others.

Variance associated with Mental-Social Simulation is not *less than* what exists in the Universal level of resolution. Variance between and within Mental-Social Simulations manifests as broad differences during interactions with society. The variance is undoubtedly perceivable from base reality. Further, the Social Simulation would exhibit variance to a degreé perceptible within the Simulation too.

Such variance is a side effect of iterations of Mental-Social Simulation not loading the same subsets of social elements and constructions. This is like what leads to variance in the Mental-Universal context. Meaning, reloading or otherwise changing social elements within the span of a Simulation runtime leads to residual variance.

The notion of residue is something new but is not without context. In computing, especially when it comes to storage, there are residual bits on the substrate leftover from prior computation. Permanent destruction of stored bits requires physical destruction of the computing substrate.

I think the frequency of repetition in the Mental-Social Simulation stems from the finite set of Social experiences and interactions usable by the Mental substrate. If there are only five potential Social constructs but the Mental substrate instantiates six, at least one of the five is a repeat. Computationally, this is a classic *pigeonhole problem*. It goes without saying a collision of this nature is undesirable.

The Mental substrate could change associated Social elements to mitigate the impact of potential collisions. This is something the Programmer would have implemented in the foundational fabric of the substrate. Such change would perturb the Social foreground in a noticeable manner. Considering the feasibility of Social experience or interaction collision, I think noticeable change would manifest as a duplication. This is not necessarily déjà vu though because the events are not identical.

The Mental-Social fidelity acts as an antidote to potential pigeonhole collisions. The substrate harnesses the fidelity of its own Simulations to effectively manage its complexity. To do so, the architecture adds a new governor or watcher feature. Asserting such a feature is quite the innovation compared to the Actual and Virtual types. Now there is an embedded component capable of using fidelity to allocate compute resources dynamically. This is worth exploring in terms of the five aspects of Simulation fidelity.

The Mental-Social resolution fluctuates as the substrate expends compute resources to instantiate nested Simulations and manage potential collisions. The opposing ends of the fluctuation would be the Universal on one side and the Social on the other. Overall Simulation resolution might be comparable to a picture-in-picture TV setup rather than an embedded small TV or the Mental-Universal modal. Further, the TV and picture-in-picture can change channels simultaneously and independently.

It should not be a surprise to discover high error rates in the Mental-Social artifact. I don't think the error rates are consistently higher. The errors burst higher alongside the resolution fluctuations. The Social Simulation expresses these error bursts throughout the social fabric. This would be extremely noticeable. However, the larger impact to accuracy of the Mental-Social Simulation would be significant when a pigeonhole collision occurs. The Mandela effect discussed in the *A Glitch in the Matrix* documentary is an example of how such a collision manifests.

I think the Mental-Social substrate leverages the new governor mechanism to quickly teardown the affected Simulation and instantiate a replacement. This would be infeasible because the substrate is monitoring the fidelity so closely. Such a correction would cause disruptive ripples in the precision of the Simulation though.

The degree of sensitivity fluctuates in synchronization with the overall Social artifact coming in and out of the Mental substrate's *focus.* This is like elements crossing the Mental-Universal modal border. The difference though is the Mental-Social has sensitivity measures applied to Social interaction. As such, the fidelity emerges from element level interaction within the Social context. This follows the resolution fluctuations rather than the elements crossing a border.

At the same time, I suspect the Mental-Social extends the idea of embodied Programmers. The extension builds on nested Mental substrates by adding a capability for cross-Social communication of precision. Again, the new governor component facilitates this addition. The cost of the addition becomes a net precision loss when viewed from the base reality segment of the core Mental substrate. This makes me think the Mental-Social is the start of having isolated Simulations which are self-sustaining, self-managing, and dynamically self-instantiating.

§2.3 When?

The Social level of resolution simulates *when* as a byproduct of time. In the previous Simulation types time began and ended with a link to the base reality Machine tick rate. However, in the Mental Simulation type *when* is not such an easy artifact to unpack. We no longer have a distinction between backdrop and Simulation clocks. We have at a minimum a multitude of clocks emerging from as many hypervisors are instantiating Social Simulations. Each substrate which nests those hypervisors is tracking a tick rate independent of its origin substrate.

There can be a multitude of hypervisors. We discovered this in our exploration of how Mental-Universal manifests. Time can exist as a multitude of clocks across these hypervisors. The Mental origin substrate enveloping a Mental-Social substrate tracks *when* for itself and passes time linearly as a value into nested Simulations. The Simulation generates time as an imagined artifact at the level of an individual. The individual then imagines how time functions across a society.

The chief differences in Mental-Social Simulation are pinning and threading. The threading takes on a more traditional multi-threaded concurrency architecture with threads spanning laterally across any given substrate. Lateral concurrency comes into play because of each Simulation having itself, individual societies, individual social constructs within societies, and whatever nested substrates may exist. Time becomes subdivided as a result. Each subdivisions pins time independently in relation to the overall Simulation.

§2.4 Constraints

The Mental instantiation of the Social drives constraints applicable at this level of resolution. I don't think the set of applicable constraints is necessarily different than what we've discussed in other Social Simulation contexts. I think the Mental Simulation is constrained by base reality natural law but only insofar as the Mental substrate perceives social norms and society writ large against the Universal background. I also don't think social norms as Simulation constraints can be *imagined* if the constraints are absent from base reality and the hypervisor. I would concede the Mental substrate can select which norms to apply though.

I do think the integration of the constraints is going to be logically different. The expansion of substrate and virtualization complexity will force some variation in integration points. As well as the architectural shift in threading and pinning undergirding time may lead to integration changes if not just more sophisticated constraint application.

The meaningful distinction between the Social and previous Mental-Universal Simulation resolution is the complexity. I see the complexity as situated in the Mental-

Social as a nested artifact within the Universal. This means compute resources feed the Social artifact as a focal point.

I wonder to what extent a nested Mental-Social Simulation is able simulate its own versions of compute power, energy, and storage. I realize how strange the assertion may seem but encourage us to think critically about such a concept for a moment. The idea isn't without precedence- modern virtualization *simulates* energy for example. We can send or withdraw virtualization energy just as well as we can send or withdraw energy to the underlying physical substrate. Modern virtualization simulates compute power stemming from such energy. Why couldn't a Mental substrate *aware* (i.e., capable of mental virtualization) do the same?

Storage is where we see further advancements in constraints. In simplest terms, a traditional storage fabric would be too slow in the face of the extreme compute I/O[32] beginning to ramp up in conjunction with the Mental substrate architecture. As an alternative, I wonder if some version of RAM Disk is more appropriate as such would be orders of magnitude faster. I can foresee two side effects. RAM is not persistent storage. As well, the signal-communication constraint needs to change to remain in concordance with the compute resources.

I don't think the constraint architecture needs to change to remain aligned with compute power or storage. We are still discussing the fundamental constraints applying to a nested T-joint structure. I suppose the signal-communication endpoint on the Simulation side must operate at a higher frequency compared to the preceding Simulation types. I also suspect the *wiring* needs to accommodate the difference say between traditional storage fabrics and a RAM disk framework.

---

[32] Although I/O is an acronym for *input* and *output,* I opted to not use the full terms to distinguish the use here from input and output filtering as a Simulation fidelity artifact. The I/O in this context is specific to the signaling between compute components.

Optical or graphene-based signal bus structures might do the trick. These would maintain necessary signal-communication speeds. These would also permit dynamic redirection or soft re-wiring associated with the spontaneous demands of the Mental-Social substrate. Either option would lead to a more developed differentiation in the interoperability and extensibility of the Mental-Social.

The Social level of resolution exists within the Universal framework. We can imagine the Social unfolding within the boundaries of the Universal as we might watch particles falling in a snow globe. The Social is extensible within the confinement of the Simulation in the same way that you might change a character in the snow globe. A minor but material differentiation from the Universal resolution though is any extension made to the Social indubitably must have effects rippled upstream. Computationally, we can conceive of this idea as a change to a software function that has effects on input and output.

In line with this reasoning, as much as a snow globe universe is computationally interoperable with alternative bases and substrates, the Social within is interoperable with the plethora of instantiating constructs. This mirrors the T-joint interlocked with T-joint mechanism displayed in the signaling and communication. There is also a clue pointing us towards how the Mental-Virtual implements the integrity checking constraint.

I think we are close to the limits of what is possible with an integrity checking constraint. The components and artifacts solid enough to produce an integrity characteristic ends with the Social. Within the Social artifact, even if integrity checking were possible- which is dubious- I would not trust it. More to the point, I wouldn't trust any integrity values nested past the initial Mental-Social Simulation because of the ability for the Mental substrates below to manufacture sub-Simulations including the state of those substrates.

§3 Mental Simulation: Individual Level of Resolution

Mental Simulation has the resolution of the Individual when a simulated Individual simulates the experience of being an Individual. In other words, the Mental-Individual is a Simulation of a computational object with the capacity to internally simulate what it is to be a *real* computational object. This is an extreme push against both theory and application.

Let's take the Mental-Social concept of an NPC further. Imagine the NPCs are empty vessels but have the capacity to execute a Mental Simulation substrate. The Simulation does not use pre-programmed or scripted behavior. The simulated Mental Individual (the subject of this section) also possesses nested Mental Simulations at all three levels of resolutions. Such Simulations can manifest further nested Simulations. The recursion could be without end.

The potential ramifications of the open-ended scaling are powerful enough to almost warrant their own chapter. For that reason, the description of how the Mental-Individual Simulation Function achieves instantiation and what precisely it simulates is critical. As well, I want to give proper attention to what is being simulated insofar as those artifacts may reveal a great deal of the uniqueness of this type and level of resolution.

§3.1 How?

The pure computational theory description for the Individual resolution in the Mental type is a computer program that writes other computer programs. Mental Simulation at the Individual level of resolution is tantamount to a computer program writing another program that outputs values interpretable as an Individual[33]. How the Mental-Individual Simulation is instantiated is at once the most complex architecture we

---

[33] In classical computation, we are describing a Universal Turing Machine.

have encountered so far and the most diverse in its capability for Simulation. The best way to tease apart the complexity in this context is to start with the substrate underlying the level of resolution.

One way to conceptualize the substrate for Mental Simulation at the level of Individual resolution would be to think about a synthetic brain. I use the term synthetic instead of artificial because I do not want to confuse the substrate here with popular ideas of conscious machines, sentient artificial intelligences, and so forth. I prefer synthetic because it denotes imitation rather than a forged copy.

The Mental-Individual is imitating the Mental substrate abstractly. This Simulation is the Mental-Universal, Mental-Social, and itself all at the same time. I cannot overstatement just how powerful this substrate arrangement is in terms of the ability to produce Simulation. For now, let us imagine the synthetic brain (Mental) constructing a plethora of mixed Simulation type substrates itself and using those to instantiate nested Simulations. There would be a Simulation Function with selection algorithms at each junction of substrate and Simulation. The synthetic Mental *codes* these in real time.

There is no way around it. This substrate architecture is tremendously complex. We should consider the geometry representing Mental-Individual as something like a mesh nested in or layered on a mesh to simplify our approach. The geometry crosses the boundary from three-dimensional to four spatial dimensions because the nested or layering could continue near infinitely (Fig. 9).

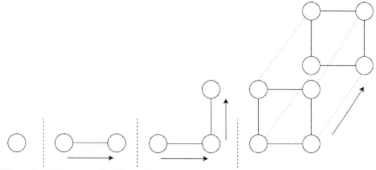

Fig. 9: The evolution from one dimension to four spatial dimensions

The virtualization stack needs to be commensurately capable if the Mental Simulation at the Individual level of resolution can instantiate sub-virtualized Mental states. I think it is safe to imagine the disparity in technological advancement from all previous Simulation types to what we described as Mental-Social Simulation is at least the same distance between the Social level of resolution and Mental-Individual. Let us further assume the Mental-Individual fully can instantiate an infinite number of sub-virtualizations. It is natural to wonder *how* the Mental-Individual virtualization works. I foresee two possibilities and the two may not be exclusive.

Any such states function like *containers* as one possibility. Containers are like the *seamless mode* virtualization introduced in the Mental-Social context. However, containers lack operating system virtualization. Containers trade virtualization for tight coupling to the container host. In exchange, containers are flexible, compute efficient, and massively scalable.

The other possibility is similar to the modern infrastructure-as-a-service architectural model. The general name for this is *cloud* architecture. The difference here is that cloud abstracts a collective of hardware into a general compute fabric. Cloud uses the compute fabric to instantiate virtualized infrastructure components with the benefit of the components being flexible, compute efficient, and quite scalable.

If that reads like what we just established with containers, it should. Again, the two possibilities do not exist in a *choose one or the other* context. In fact, given just how complex the Mental-Individual Simulation appears, I suspect each instantiated Mental-Individual Simulation operates within a unified container. Unified meaning all Simulation components are together. There is no separation between backdrop and foreground. The substrate instantiates the container or containers through a cloud-like fabric.

The technical aspects of this follows the substrate architecture we have outlined and opens the potential for the input-output filtering artifacts to provide the Individual level of resolution customization necessary for unique Mental experiences.

The Mental-Individual Simulation, put simply, has apertures, Selection Functions, and input-output filtering *everywhere*. By everywhere, I mean the three artifacts are present alongside each Type 2 hypervisor substrate. Thus, there is at least two sets but there could be an unlimited quantity at the maximum extreme.

Compared to the Social level of resolution, the Simulation Function can program Mental-Individual substrates during instantiation. The just-in-time programmable substrate concept is further advanced in the Individual level of resolution. The virtualization stack can construct apertures, Selection Functions, and input-output filters dynamically. Each instantiated Mental state customizes the input-output filtering architecture.

While this seems inordinately complex even to me, I don't see any other means to account for the variety and richness of the Mental-Individual Simulation. At the same time there are solid technological foundations pointing towards the validity of such architectures.

§3.2 What?

The Mental-Individual Simulation is at once familiar and strange. The Individual is familiar because it is the closest level of resolution to our first-hand experience. At the same time there is a strangeness permeating the notion of the Mental-Individual Simulation. The Individual is a source for what the Individual perceives within the Mental Simulation. The Individual is also what the Mental substrate simulates. In other words, the Individual becomes a wellspring for the elements and constructs it itself perceives. It is simultaneously also a Simulation of potentially *other* elements and constructs. The Simulation computationally ought to exhibit new forms of variance, repetition, change, and fidelity.

I strongly believe one term to describe the variance exhibited in Mental Simulation at the Individual level of resolution is *chaotic*. Strangely, I think the internal chaos is so constant and normalized the perception of the Individual of itself is one of stability. An apt analogy would be the stroboscopic effect seen in spoked wheels. I think variance in this Simulation would not necessarily be evident to viewers located in base reality just as the wheel seems to not be rotating to the observer. The Simulation would generate the experience of variance within itself.

The extreme dynamicism associated with nested substrates, logic within the Simulation Functions, and Selection Functions drive the chaotic variance. In simple terms, variance is what makes the Individual existence. I do not see this variance as anything other than intentionally programmed. The variance operates as a form of sub-Simulation. If true, this notion of intentionally programmed sub-Simulation extends further.

Given the enveloping variance present in this type of Simulation, changes to the Simulation would be both frequent and disruptive to the phenomenology of the Individual. In fact, we might perceive repetition and change as part of the Simulation rather than something external to the Simulation because of their frequency. Of course, some repetition and change could be so impactful as to be disruptive in a perceivable manner.

What I find compelling about the Mental-Individual concept is that the Mental substrate can function as its own Programmer by proxy. This gives rise to a computational foundation for the levels of repetition and change I just mentioned insofar as the embedded Programmer capability in the substrate may act as a procedural generation instrument. Procedural generation has had remarkable success in modern computing. The technology uses a limited base input and generates an infinite number of variations. This strikes me as comporting with how the hypervisor seeds the Mental substrate with fundamental elements of base reality rather than receiving a full input stream of base reality.

I want to use the term *volatile* as it accurately captures the computational intention. More explicitly, the elements within one's field of view would be the only Simulation objects with fidelity. Anything not under active perception of the individual would be just background noise and filtered out of view. In fact, the set of elements not actively perceived may not be instantiated into the Simulation at all.

The Glitch in the Matrix documentary illustrates this well when introducing the notion of draw distance and partial rendering in video games. I can see how draw distance and partial rendering connect to procedural generation. These are motive forces for repetition and change in the Mental-Individual Simulation.

I suspect the notion of computational volatility is immediately perceptible in the rendered resolution of the Mental-Individual Simulation. In the Actual and Virtual Simulation types, our TV maintained a constant resolution albeit at various levels of fidelity. The Mental-Individual Simulation would not only have dynamic variability in its resolution, but each nested Simulation would have different resolutions. Each would also have the potential for isolated variation in error and accuracy.

The observable and experienced *glitches* discussed throughout the source material are examples of errors and accuracy in the Mental-Individual Simulation. One reason undergirding the Mental-Individual experience of these glitches is the inability for the Simulation architecture to fully track all the spawning, multithreaded, and abstracted compute resources funneling in and out of the substrates.

I suggest error rates and accuracy operate in a unique way compared to all prior Simulation artifacts. The Actual, Virtual, and previous Mental Simulations exercised fidelity at the elemental level in terms of errors and accuracy. I contend the Mental-Individual manifests these more abstractly. Consider the black cat crossing the doorway twice in *The Matrix* movie and think about the level at which such a glitch exists. The level is like a collection of elements, bound to time, and associated with a background thread passing into the Simulation foreground. This passing of threaded processes is in fact how a compute substrate context switches a computational operation. Interesting.

On one hand, the precision of the Mental Simulation at the Individual level of resolution would be exacting. Yet, on the other hand, I am not certain the precision is as much intentional as it is uncontrolled happenstance. The instantiated Mental-Individual perturbs the enveloping Simulation fabric simply by thinking let alone interacting with it. This level of sensitivity is extreme. I am not convinced it is a *conscious* Mental instantiation as much as it is a byproduct of having such a hyper-connected, hyper-nested substrate and virtualization architecture underneath the Simulation.

§3.3 When?

Time is fluid in the Mental-Individual Simulation. The concept of time might be chaotic in fact. To be clear, I'm referring to the tick rate of time as the Mental substrate implements it. This extends to the nested Individual substrate as well. We can call this *simulated time,* so we have a label to track the artifact during the ensuing discussion.

The Simulation does not synchronize tick rate across itself or subordinate Simulations. Oscillations between Mental and nested Individual will inevitably experience drift just as the multitude of clocks do in our modern world. As well, like in our modern world, there must be an independent and objective source of time. All clocks use such an authoritative source to periodically resynchronize. I suspect the base reality Machine continues to hold a constant tick relative to the universe it resides in and has a synchronization interface exposed through the physical substrate.

Meanwhile, the Mental Simulation exacerbates the fluidity of the time artifact with its fleeting perceptions. The Individual perception of time can be divorced from the real passing rate of time. There would be a waxing and waning of tick rate synchrony between base reality, Machine, and upwards through the full stack of substrates into the perception layer.

The Individual level of resolution would impart a distinct perception of synchronicity to the Mental Simulation. I suspect this to be true because of the probabilities at work governing the variance and outputs within the Simulation. Put simply, the chance of the same individual perceiving the same simulated content or events across time in identical ways is nonzero. These synchronistic events would be immediately perceptible.

The Mental-Individual has a slippery handle on its perception of events situated within the simulated timeline. This is true whether the perception is déjà vu, Mandela effects, or a version of Butterly chaos. For this reason, we need to develop a robust understanding of how constraints apply to this type and level of Simulation.

§3.4 Constraints

Constraints on the Individual level of resolution in Mental Simulation would be slippery to say the least. The ability for the individual to manifest experience across perception boundaries appears to bypass constraints despite constraints being in place. I think this type and level of Simulation might seem as if the constraints do not apply. Once resources such as compute power, energy, and storage are sufficiently available to make Mental-individual Simulation possible, I doubt there are limitations above and beyond. We should not take this to mean there are no constraints at all though.

The problem is there is no computational foundation for how constraints operate in this type and level of Simulation. However, the lack of precedence should not preclude the possibility. The best guess I have is the Individual level of resolution would be instantiated in a polymorphic modality. Polymorphism can take on a variety of definitions and it behooves us to be clear with our usage. I suggest polymorphism is the use of an abstract symbol to represent a multitude of types. In computation, a *type* is an integer, a string, or a collection of such types.

Thus, polymorphism acts as a mechanism to allow for the overarching Simulation to fluctuate between types and resolutions. In other words, constraints exist, constraints apply to Mental-Individual Simulation, but these constraints are polymorphic since Mental-Individual itself is polymorphic.

The compute power, energy, and storage necessary to conduct Mental Simulation at the Individual level of resolution is not what we might expect. I say this because the Mental-Individual is fundamentally visualizing and virtualizing itself.

As an example, imagine a color. There is the color as it is and the color as you perceive it. Where a given green may have an intensity of say four, your perception of that same green might be six because you really like green or your conscious rendering upscales it. The more crucial point is perceiving the color as a four or six does not tell us anything about the real color. We can only know the instantiation of the color as we see it.

I use this example because I think the Mental-Individual Simulation is only constrained by what the Mental substrate can conceive. This is the same idea presented in the Mental-Social artifact. The idea is now writ large for the Individual level of resolution. Further, I feel comfortable with this idea because the previous Simulation types established the fundamental components. The difference is we were working with traditional, monolithic structures in previous Simulation types and resolutions. We now have massively multithreaded, concurrent, and polymorphic architectures.

Signaling and communication are not error-free at the Individual level of resolution. Even computationally advanced signal-communication architecture has limits under constraint. At the same time, I don't know that errors are exceptions to the Mental-Individual experience. In part due to the architecture and in part because of the nature of the Mental-Individual Simulation, I suggest there could be significant loss and jitter.

It seems obvious more frequent signaling and communication error conditions will arise as more hypervisors become nested within other hypervisors. I do think signaling and communication are dependable even with the requirement for dynamic, real-time transmission alongside the probability for errors. Significant errors in loss and jitter do not cause the Mental-Individual Simulation to fail. This is also why such errors may produce perceptible *glitches* in the Simulation.

A Mental Simulation at the Individual level of resolution guarantees interoperability. Mental-Individual Simulations interchange across different hypervisors and different substrates. Changing the underlying Mental hypervisor does not interrupt *service* to the above layers in the virtualization stack. This isn't to suggest no glitch would occur in the perception of the Mental-Individual. The Simulation interchange could happen in real time without interruption to the simulated individual nested substrate or the Simulation of the experience of the individual. Every Mental-Individual Simulation would be infinitely extensible. The idea of infinitely in this context is not entirely hyperbolic. I sincerely do not know whether any limits exist.

Accordingly, integrity checking in the Mental-Individual Simulation would be difficult to say the least. There is a strong temptation to hand wave integrity away at this point. We shouldn't give up though.

No, we should rely on the nature of computational objects to guide us towards a solution. We know Mental Simulation at the Individual resolution is still computational. The Mental computation is materially and significantly different than any other Simulation we've explored. We also know the Mental-Individual has the capability of dynamically instantiated nested Simulations and combinations of Simulation artifacts. Those are all computational objects too.

The base reality Machine can affirm the integrity of its substrate. The Machine substrate imparts this ability to the Mental Type 2 hypervisor and from there to all subordinate hypervisors instantiated as nested substrates. Despite all of that, the Mental-Individual resolution is simply too volatile, too dynamic to leverage a traditional integrity checking mechanism. The Individual Simulation has a computational *intuition* of internal consistency though.

I might compare such internal consistency intuition to *fuzzy logic*. More formally, we can think about fuzzy logic as a type of heuristics-based reasoning. In some sense what I'm suggesting is that integrity in the classical sense may not apply here or even be necessary. Alternatively, the Mental-Individual Simulation leverages the power imparted by its computational nature to track what adjacent components the substrate tethers to or spawns from it.

Furthermore, what if an embedded computational object provides integrity checking instead of the hypervisor or substrate applied integrity to the Simulation? The embedded object might be an augmentative artificial intelligence agent. The agent checks integrity elements within the Mental-Individual Simulation as those elements are instantiated and destroyed. The agent would itself be immutable though. The Individual Simulation could not *write* to it, just *read* from it. Integrity measurement transmits through a background link between the core hypervisor and this agent. We can refer to this as the Mental-Individual *conscience.*

Dr. Scalambrino

Philosophically speaking, all levels of resolution regarding a "mental" type of Simulation, in Simulation theory, refer to the idea that the mental part of our experience of reality is the experience of a Simulation. At the same time, as noted at the end of the above chapter on Virtual Simulation, Mental Simulation need not necessarily be understood simply as the difference between a mental dimension and an actual dimension. This is the case for two reasons, which may be, respectively, called: mental monism and Cartesian dualism.

First, mental monism is one way to understand the mental. So, it is possible to understand the mental as if there is no other dimension to which a "base reality" could refer. Second, because "mental" tends to suggest a kind of individuation (for example, the mind of an individual), Cartesian dualism tends to naturally follow for many who set out to understand the "mental" type of Simulation in Simulation theory.

Cartesian dualism will be discussed below; therefore, suffice to say here that it refers to an idea that though there may be another dimension than the mental, the mental dimension is understood as primary, and the reality of the second kind of substance or dimension may remain ultimately ambiguous (for example, as if it were an illusion or the trick of an evil genius).

To begin, then, here, again, invoking Morpheus' distinction is helpful. In this way, the difference with Mental Simulation is that it allows for the changing of an individual into an agent of the Matrix in such a way that the individual is annihilated by the change. Virtual Simulation, due to its difference from Actual Simulation, allows for every actual individual to potentially unplug.

Just as Actual Simulation is ontologically ambiguous regarding this constraints and transcendence question, so too Mental Simulation remains soteriologically ambiguous. For example, it is not clear whether being annihilated from a Simulation is necessarily negative. There are multiple instances in which one could see being annihilated from a Simulation as good, as desirable, and as a kind of blessing. So, regarding constraints and transcendence, Mental Simulation is ultimately ambiguous.

I'd like to structure the beginning of my portion of this chapter by pointing to a set of scenes from the fourth *Matrix* film, *The Matrix: Resurrections*. Those scenes occur at: (1) 27 minutes & 7 seconds, (2) 37minutes & 40 seconds, (3) 55 minutes & 8 seconds, (4) 1hour, 25 minutes & 44 seconds, (5) 2 hours, zero minutes & 53 seconds, (6) 2 hours, 15 minutes & 20 seconds. For additional mnemonic convenience, I have named them the following: (1) Trinity's determinism puzzle, (2) Neo's self-doubt puzzle, (3) Morpheus' reality puzzle, (4) the puzzle of The Merovingian's revelation, (5) Agent Smith's identity puzzle, (and 6) the puzzle of The Architect's revelation.

(1) Trinity, speaking to Neo, asks, "I remember wanting a family, but is that because that's what women are supposed to want?" "How do you know if you want something yourself or if your upbringing programmed you to want it?"

(2) Neo, speaking to the Architect asks, "Am I crazy?" To which The Analyst authoritatively responds, "We don't use that word in here."

(3) Morpheus poses the following question for Neo, "Is reality based in memory nothing but fiction?"

(4) The Merovingian states, "We had grace; we had style; we had conversation! Not this beep beep beep beep [moving his thumbs, as if texting]."

(5) Agent Smith, after killing The Architect, says to Neo, "You know the difference between us? Anyone could have been you, whereas I've always been anyone."

(6) The Architect, speaking to Trinity and Neo, states "'Go for it!' Knock yourselves out. Paint the sky with rainbows, but here's the thing the sheeple aren't going anywhere. They like my world. They don't want this senti-mentality. They don't want freedom or empowerment. They want to be controlled. They crave the comfort of certainty. And, that means you two back in your pods, unconscious and alone, just like them."

To which Neo & Trinity, chuckling, respond, "We're not here to negotiate anything. We're on our way to change your world... [to] just remind people what a free mind can do."

As will be shown and discussed below, these puzzles span a spectrum from least to most ontological and soteriological ambiguity. It is tempting to divide these six puzzles into three parts, assigning two puzzles to each type of Simulation; however, a number of the puzzles are symbolically pregnant enough to be meaningful for multiple types of Simulation. It will be by way of discussing these puzzles, below, that both Simulation theory, in general, and Mental Simulation, in particular, may be explicated.

§4 Mental Simulation: Universal Level of Resolution

In sum, and philosophically speaking: The "Mental Simulation" level of resolution in Simulation Theory refers to the idea that the content of our minds may be governed by an external power in a way that alienates us from our be-ing to the extent that it inserts us into a Simulation. At each level of resolution, then, regarding Mental Simulation, there is the question of how the mind, and – even better – the soul, relates to Simulation. Perhaps the best way to order these ideas is in terms of the *Welt*-ing process. Thus, Mental Simulation at the level of the universal requires the consideration of other minds, and the consideration of one's own mind, as parts of a Simulation. In this way, the *Um-Welt* and *Mit-Welt* function as a ground and spring for the *Selbst-Welt* and *Eigen-Welt*. This is reversed to: *Selbst-Welt* and *Eigen-Welt* functioning as a ground and spring for the *Um-Welt* and *Mit-Welt* in the individual level of resolution. The social level of revolution, then, takes the *Mit-Welt* as primary with the order of the other three left ontologically ambiguous.

Recall our discussion from Chapter 2, §6, above: Whereas Morpheus' distinction is a *necessary* component of the ontological structure of Virtual Simulation, it is *ambiguous* regarding the ontological structure of Actual Simulation. In other words, the "How?" question regarding Virtual Simulation at the individual level must allow for the possibility that all actual individuals (located in base reality and) participating in the Virtual Simulation must be able to "unplug" from (i.e., transcend the) Simulation.

Now, the reason that Mental Simulation is more complicated is because of an ontological ambiguity concerning its identity. This ontological ambiguity is peculiar to Mental Simulation in that all thought may be considered evidence of simulated activity. In other words, Mental Simulation collapses the observer-observed distinction; it ignores the boundary between individuals (This is why the *Selbst-Welt* was considered more primary than the *Eigen-Welt*, above). More bluntly, that the mind itself may be understood as a Simulation is a hallmark, in Simulation theory, of Mental Simulation. This allows for a soteriological ambiguity regarding Mental Simulation as well. Both of these ideas will be discussed below.

Yet, this can be summed here by referring to an external power that is somehow governing individual minds, because of the peculiar ontological ambiguity and the, subsequent, soteriological ambiguity constituting Mental Simulation in Simulation theory. Soteriologically speaking, Actual Simulation does not have access to base reality, virtual, does, and for the mental level it is ambiguous. It is, ontologically, "undecideable" in that even a feedback loop with feeling may be considered Simulations.

Thus, keeping in mind that Morpheus' distinction may be understood soteriologically, we see precisely how Mental Simulation is distinguished from actual and Virtual Simulation, especially the individual level of resolution of Virtual Simulation. Hence, just as we can envision a spectrum along which a person's will may be more or less "hijacked" ("hacked"), so too a person's mind.

§4.1 How?

To ask, then, "How" a Mental Simulation is possible, philosophically, is to focus on the different ways to understand "Mental" and how those different understandings shape our further understanding of their relation to base reality. Thus, in regard to the universal level of resolution, the Mental must be understood in a universal way. There are two primary ways to interpret and understand how the Mental can be universal. These two ways are, precisely, the two ways in which the ontological ambiguity (pointed out by Morpheus' distinction) can be resolved. That is to say, base reality may be understood as mind-external and Actual or as completely Mental.

The former interpretation, by way of a mind-external base reality, resolves any soteriological ambiguity, such that so long as individual minds are understood as grounded in actuality, and so long as actuality is not understood as itself being a part of the Simulation, then those minds can be saved from a Mental Simulation by becoming less alienated from their actual being. Yet, the latter, pan-psychic or pan-mental interpretation, neither resolves the ontological nor the soteriological ambiguity associated with the mental type of Simulation.

Trinity's puzzle is applicable here. And, Trinity's puzzle may be framed according to both interpretations. Trinity's puzzle asks "I remember wanting a family, but is that because that's what women are supposed to want?" "How do you know if you want something yourself or if your upbringing programmed you to want it?" According to the mind-external interpretation, even if one is "programmed" by nature or nurture, we would also have enough ontological freedom to be able to resist being controlled by a Simulation. According to the pan-mental interpretation, it doesn't appear as though one would be able to resist the programming of the Simulation.

As I discuss in *What Is Existentialism?* Volumes I & II (2021), this is directly analogous to the difference between the concepts of destiny and fate, respectively. Moreover, Trinity's puzzle may be characterized by an exclusively genetic model or a more biosocial one. So, perhaps a valuable idea to invoke here, then, is Erickson's idea of developmental stages. For, these stages could be understood as exclusively genetic or as more biosocial.

Just as "programming" may be understood as a double entendre, so too the two understandings are precisely the two interpretations just noted. Perhaps, the most common ways we find these two interpretations articulated are in terms of the actual (base reality) as biological – the former interpretation – and the mental as base reality in terms of an "all is mind" – the latter interpretation –, understanding of reality. Notice, the latter, pan-mental, interpretation does not resolve the soteriological ambiguity associated with Mental Simulation. In other words, this latter interpretation does not resolve the ambiguities resolved by the former; that is to say, a pan-mental ontology in Simulation theory, ontologically, leaves open the possibility that the mind itself is a/the Simulation, and, soteriologically, it is unclear what transcendence from such a pan-Mental Simulation might look like.

Hence, we can draw a number of conclusions here regarding the "How?" of Mental Simulation at the universal level of resolution. First, if we understand universal Mental Simulation as involving a mind-external base reality, then we can either understand the actuality as not ultimately mental or as ultimately mental, in the sense of a pan-mental ontology. Soteriologically speaking, so long as there is a base reality outside of the mental, then such an ontology itself answers the question of transcendence regarding Mental Simulation at the universal level of resolution.

However, a pan-mental ontology shrouds the universal level's soteriology in ambiguity, since it is not clear what salvation from such an ontology would be. If mind is all there is, then it is not clear what transcendence from such an ontology would be. Lastly, if we understand "programming" in the context of an ontology that includes a mind-external dimension, then "upbringing," in Trinity's puzzle, may be understood as a hypervisor leading to a plugging-into a Simulation.

Before moving on to the next section, we should consider how Neo's self-doubt puzzle relates to what has already been said. Recall, from *The Matrix: Resurrections*, that Neo, speaking to the Architect asks, "Am I crazy?" To which The Analyst authoritatively responds, "We don't use that word in here." Of course, the "in here" could be understood as pointing to the Simulation. Yet, the following two thoughts are more important for us to notice, here: "Crazy" is slang for some significant deviation from a norm. So, on the one hand, a pan-mental understanding of reality necessarily rejects the idea of deviation from a norm, since the system being normed is a Simulation and there is nothing outside of the Simulation.

On the other hand, we can understand the base reality of a Mental Simulation in a more soteriologically-favorable way. Consider an analogy with x, y & z axes. Norms on the x & y axis lose their prescriptive value as soon as one recognizes the biases in their sampling. If a transcended point of view relates from a completely different dimension, then it is not that the norms of the Simulation are wrong, rather it is that the norms of the Simulation pertain to a dimension of reality that we are not. A dimension of reality by way of which we are controlled. Hence, this ontological difference would allow for us to understand transcendence in terms of alienation from one's true be-ing.

§4.2 When?

Following the initial distinction between a pan-mental versus a non-pan-mental understanding of Mental Simulation, the question "When?" can either be answered or not. Here we can see this difference by juxtaposing the Morpheus puzzle with The Merovingian puzzle. On the one hand, Morpheus posed the following question for Neo, "Is reality based in memory nothing but fiction?" And, if we understand Mental Simulation as pan-mental, then we cannot know the answer to the question "When?" because there is no temporal base-reality from which to establish a norm or timeline. On the other hand, it may be possible for some beings to discern the shifts in the Simulation and consider them as on a timeline. Whether this Simulation-based timeline is a line, a portion of a circle, or an illusion, cannot be determined in a pan-mental ontology.

The Merovingian's puzzle illustrates the idea of temporal awareness through witnessing paradigm shifts within a Simulation. For example, the Merovingian pointed out, "We had grace; we had style; we had conversation! Not this beep beep beep beep [moving his thumbs, as if texting]." Whether we consider an increase in technological mediation to be positively correlated with alienation from one's true be-ing or not, shifts in modes of production and technology may be understood as sufficiently significant enough shifts in the Simulation to be able to formulate an answer to the question "When?"

§4.3 Constraints

In this way, we are constrained from knowing time just as we are constrained from fully being able to articulate a necessary ontology for Mental Simulation. Yet, there is one constraint that may point to a kind of awareness that may, further, suggest a possible transcendence, and that is the Agent Smith puzzle.

In *The Matrix: Resurrections*, after killing The Architect, Agent Smith, said to Neo, "You know the difference between us? Anyone could have been you, whereas I've always been anyone." As we will see, thinking through Agent Smith's puzzle provides some clarity regarding the soteriology of Mental Simulation.

§4.4 Transcendence

What Agent Smith's puzzle shows is that even within a pan-mental ontology, there can be significant difference between agents of the Simulation and agents that are somehow different from simulated agents, that is, from simulated agencies. Though this provides some clarity soteriologically, it does not provide clarity regarding ontology. The idea, then, is that even if we cannot speak of a dimension outside, or external to, to Simulation, we may still be able to speak of transcendence. In other words, alienation from one's true be-ing has reference, even if we are not certain to what it refers.

In *The Matrix: Resurrections*, The Architect's puzzle may be understood as invoking just such a solution. Speaking to Trinity and Neo, The Architect stated "'Go for it!' Knock yourselves out. Paint the sky with rainbows, but here's the thing the sheeple aren't going anywhere. They like my world. They don't want this senti-mentality. They don't want freedom or empowerment. They want to be controlled. They crave the comfort of certainty. And, that means you two back in your pods, unconscious and alone, just like them." To which Neo & Trinity, chuckling, respond, "We're not here to negotiate anything. We're on our way to change your world... [to] just remind people what a free mind can do."

The solution, articulated by Trinity and Neo, amounts – in terms of Simulation theory – to a statement that there is potential for transcendence, for some kind of transcendence, even if the Mental Simulation in which one exists has a pan-mental ontology. And, as already noted above, Mental Simulation with a mind-external ontology, then transcendence is possible through liberation *from* the Simulation *toward* mind-external base reality.

§5 Mental Simulation: Social Level of Resolution

In regard to Mental Simulation, the social level of resolution is probably the most intuitive and easy to understand of Mental Simulation's three levels of resolution. Just as the universal level could be understood in terms of mind-external and pan-mental ontologies, on the one hand, the social level can be understood as a Simulation by way of which *the minds of individuals* can be controlled; on the other hand, sociality itself may be understood as constituting the very mind that is a Simulation. Whereas the contrast between sociality and the minds of individuals amounts to a mind-external ontology, sociality itself as Mental Simulation amounts to a pan-mental ontology. Soteriologically, the difference, of course, is that, since we are talking about a social, not an universal, level of resolution, the difference between social and individual provides a structure for transcendence, as if it were a hanger upon which transcendence can be draped.

§5.1 How?

To ask, then, "How" a Mental Simulation is possible, philosophically, is to focus on the different ways to understand "mental" and how those different understandings shape our further understanding of their relation to base reality. Thus, in regard to the social level of resolution, the mental must be understood as, at least, grounded in the social. In other words, the mental must be understood as primarily grounded in the *Mit-Welt*.

There are two primary ways to understand how the mental can be social. The social level can be understood as a Simulation by way of which *the minds of individuals* can be controlled; on the other hand, sociality itself may be understood as constituting the very mind that is a Simulation. The former is perhaps best illustrated by the idea of "Capitalist exploitation," located at 25 minutes & 18 seconds, and the latter is perhaps best illustrated by the idea that society determines our identity and even, thereby, our self-identity. Importantly, that is to be understood dynamically, not merely statically. In other words, to say that society determines our identity is to say that how we think of ourselves and how we talk to ourselves is a product of the Simulation.

In this way, the "How?" would be answered in the following three ways. First, sociality itself could be how one can become plugged into a Simulation. Second, modes of production and economics could be how one can become plugged into a Simulation. Third, how one talks to one's self could be how one can become plugged into a Simulation. In regard to soteriology, the Simulation may be thought of as a kind of container, or guiding system, for free will. This is not to say that there is no way to live other than in a Simulation. Rather, in addition to alienation from one's be-ing and in addition to alienation from one's self, there is also alienation from one's capacity to choose, one's ability to freely be.

Recall, Nietzsche's famous discussion of sociality as the ground of consciousness such that self-consciousness is a kind of illusion. In Book 5, §354, of *The Joyful Quest* [*Die Fröhliche Wissenschaft*].

> It was only as a social animal that man acquired self-consciousness...
> My idea is, as you see, that consciousness does not really belong to man's individual existence but rather to his social or herd nature; that, as follows from this, it has developed subtlety only insofar as this is required by social or herd utility.

In this way, some of what may be desired and pursued in life may depend on a form of socialization. Think of how one must be able to see themselves in a specific way in order to participate in certain styles of living or ways of life. Thus, sociality may be understood as the ground of consciousness. The *Welt*-matrix as grounded in the *Mit-Welt*. It is as if an individual is inserted into a Mental Simulation by way of adopting a frame for experience by interacting with others.

§5.2 When?

The "When?" question regarding Mental Simulation at the social level of resolution involves the question of the relation between society and time. Just as sometimes it seems like political parties have a very specific way, they would like culture to be, so too do these groups have a specific expectation for what everyday life should look like. This, of course, may even include fashion. Hence, one can envision a kind of cultural time describing a society's cultural changes. Perhaps such political parties could dial-in, and explicate, their expectations of how everyday life should be controlled.

Another strategy for approaching the "When?" question regarding Mental Simulation at the social level of resolution is to use the distinction between the social and the individual. In this way, the contrast between time determined by the individual and cultural time, or the social identity of time, may be a way of contextualizing the "When?" question. Thus, it would be as if regression or progression of the individual may be linked to the ways in which the individual participates in cultural, and social, life. It is not just social identity as Simulation, it is also relation between social identity and personal identity as characterizable in terms of time.

§5.3 Constraints

Perhaps, rather than characterize the relation between social identity and personal identity in terms of time, it may be characterized in terms of development toward transcendence. In this way, we have come full circle and, not surprisingly, we find the constraints and transcendence spectrum associated with the difference between the social level and the individual level. This is because – as we already saw with both the actual and virtual types of Simulation – the ontology of a type of Simulation either determines or leaves ambiguous the type's soteriology.

Thus, an individual may be constrained from thriving in their own individuality by being inserted into a social identity. At the same time, this need not be a blunt binary opposition between, for example, red or blue hair. The social identity into which an individual could be inserted could also be a non-identity. The key here isn't the identity, as much as it is the eclipse of one's individual be-ing when one identifies with a Mental Simulation at the social level of resolution.

It is interesting to invoke Agent Smith's puzzle here. Recall, in *The Matrix: Resurrections*, after killing The Architect, Agent Smith, said to Neo, "You know the difference between us? Anyone could have been you, whereas I've always been anyone." The agency of the Simulation can "hijack" any of the social identities found in the Simulation. In contrast, the individual is temporally and practically constrained from animating any and all of the identities made available for Mental Simulation by sociality.

§5.4 Transcendence

Because transcendence and constraints are different aspects of the soteriology of a Simulation, there seems to be a way in which an individual can transcend a Mental Simulation grounded in sociality. This involves treating the characterizations of the ontology – noted above regarding the "How?" question – of the difference between the social and the individual as constraints which can be transcended. Recall, then, the three responses to the "How?" question regarding Mental Simulation at the social level of resolution, that is, sociality itself, modes of production and economics, and self-talk.

Hence, transcendence regarding Mental Simulation at the social level of resolution may be understood in a number of ways. First, transcendence may be understood in terms of resisting herd mentality, resisting the social interpretation of life. Second, transcendence may be understood in terms of finding a sustainable lifestyle or some way to transcend an everyday life determined by capitalism. Or, third, by resisting the social mediation of one's self-talk. These kinds of transcendence may also be characterized in terms of the *Welt*-matrix.

In the first instance, it is as if the *Selbst-Welt* may be used to resist the *Mit-Welt*, with ability to freely make meaning and make choices in regard to the *Um-Welt* and the *Eigen-Welt*. In the second instance it may be the same as the first or it may be the use of the *Um-Welt* to resist the primary of the *Mit-Welt* over the *Selbst-Welt* and *Eigen-Welt*. Finally, the *Eigen-Welt* may be invoked – whether this be understood as grace, theurgy, or mindfulness – to resist the primacy of sociality.

Lastly, it is important to recall here the types of transcendence peculiar to the social level of resolution for Mental Simulation noted while discussing the "How?" question above. Transcendence may be the undoing of alienation from one's be-ing. Transcendence may be alienation from one's self, and transcendence may be alienation from one's own freedom, that is, one's capacity to choose. The Architect's puzzle may help us gain some insight into this.

Recall, The Architect's puzzle notes, in regard to "the sheeple," as opposed to the transcended: "They don't want this senti-mentality. They don't want freedom or empowerment. They want to be controlled." To which Neo & Trinity, chuckling, respond, "We're not here to negotiate anything. We're on our way to change your world… [to] just remind people what a free mind can do." Existentially, I would paraphrase this by stating: Authenticity is valuable as an end-in-itself, even if takes place in a meaningless world.[34]

---

[34] A note to Sartre's disciples here: Notice that it is *not* possible to say of authenticity that it is "a meaningless gesture or activity," because its reality, in terms of intensity and consistency, can become a phenomenon of experience, it cannot be meaningless. To think of it that way is truly to put the cart in front of the horse. The truth of authenticity is that which is prompting us to determine whether it is meaningful or not. It is truly meaningless to say that everything is meaningless, if, in fact, everything is meaningless. In other words, scientific

§6 Mental Simulation: Individual Level of Resolution

Here, we need to contrast pan-mental and mind external to articulate one last ontology. The last possible ontology to consider for Mental Simulation refers to the idea that the individual may be participating in a Simulation by participating in "the mental." This could include interpretations like: All thought takes place within a Simulation. The distinction between the mind and the individual will be the more fruitful path to take in examining this level of resolution. Moreover, as we will see, there is a problem with the idea that to think is to participate in a Simulation. In fact, it leads to an unresolvable paradox.

The pan-mental paradox can be stated as: If my thoughts are controlled by the Simulation, then the event of my becoming aware of this fact is itself also an event controlled by the Simulation. This paradox is especially problematic because if all the thought of my having some salvageable be-ing outside the Simulation amounts to is simply a thought controlled by the Simulation, then we end up with the mind being the Simulation controlling the Simulation; a Simulation controlling itself.[35]

When we recognize the distinction between the mental and the individual, then we are able to leave the being of the mind-external individual ambiguous. In this way, we have three thoughts to track: the pan-mental with the individual as merely a part, the pan-mental with the individual as different from the mental by merely being a part, and not the whole, of the pan-mental. Lastly, of course, the mind-external could be wholly other than the pan-mental, thereby, illustrating that the ontology is not pan-mental.

---

meaning-making, as evidenced by its ability to predict the future, already shows that there is meaning at some level. That meaning may be encoded in a way that is beyond our grasp or our capacity to decode; however, that doesn't mean that it is meaningless.

[35] Put another way, the problem with the pan-mental interpretation of Mental Simulation at the individual level is that it suggests that knowledge of some mind-external salvageable be-ing is an illusion.

For ease of reference, I will call this: the mereology of Mental Simulation at the individual level of resolution.

Philosophically speaking, Mental Simulation at the individual level of resolution immediately brings Rene Descartes' philosophy to mind ("I think; therefore, I am"). On the one hand, Descartes, while questioning the reality of everything, came to the conclusion that because he was able to question the reality of everything there must be a subject that exists. The logic here being that the "I" must refer to some subject that exists.

In regard to the above mereology of Mental Simulation, then, Descartes' dualism points to the middle of the three options. We can understand this by considering the larger context of the *Meditations* from which Descartes' statement comes. Thus, on the other hand, this problem in Descartes' ontology has infamously come to be known as the mind/body problem. Importantly, the mind/body problem leads directly to the "problem of other minds," it is this latter problem that we will discuss below. And, the problem of other minds may, of course, be understood as a generic and philosophical characterization of Morpheus' distinction, noted above. Moreover, the puzzle of Neo's self-*doubt* may be understood as a version of Descartes' method of hyperbolic doubt.

So, here we invoke Descartes. The peculiarity about the way ambiguity functions ontologically at this level of resolution is that it allows for solipsism. It allows for the mind of the individual to be understood solipsistically. On the one hand, this brings in Descartes. On the other hand, this is merely self-interest, as a Google search might suggest. Rather, solipsism, here, means the belief that other minds may either not exist or may have been annihilated by the agency of a Simulation.

This is precisely why this level of resolution is most often associated with mental illness, in general, or (what philosophers refer to as) schizophrenia, in particular. Briefly, then, that the individual is able to – with Descartes' method – distinguish all others from itself, is accomplished by the "I think; therefore, I am." However, just like for Descartes, it becomes clear that we cannot have the same certainty in regard to other individuals. Hence, individuals are able to arrive at the conclusion that though they exist, others may be "automatons," or, put differently, "agents of a Simulation."

§6.1 How?

Here we need to focus on the different ways to understand "mental" and how those different understandings shape our understanding of their relation to base reality. Thus, in regard to the individual level of resolution, the mental must be understood in an individual way. That means that the mental must be understood as primarily grounded in the *Selbst-Welt*. There are two primary ways to develop this understanding. First, the individual may be understood as "plugged into" a Simulation by way of the mental. Let's call this the "gaslight" understanding of Mental Simulation at the individual level of resolution. Second, the mind may be understood as itself being a Simulation. Let's call this the "paranoid schizophrenic" understanding of Mental Simulation at the individual level of resolution.

Soteriologically, then, the gaslight interpretation has less constraints than the schizophrenic interpretation, and the former also allows for a wider scope of possible ways to understand transcendence. Whereas the former is ontologically closer to the Virtual Simulation individual level of resolution, the latter is closer to what in psychiatry is considered the symptomatology of a psychotic thought disorder. With this clarification in mind, we can now briefly consider some puzzles from *The Matrix: Resurrections*.

To begin, notice the shift from the first Matrix film to the fourth involves a shift from "The Architect" to "The Analyst." This in itself suggests a shift toward the mental type of Simulation. Is this the interpretation towards which the film points us? Is it the type of Simulation envisioned by the film's creators? Of course, even if it is not the latter, it could still be the former (cf. Barthes, 1978).

Whereas both Neo's and Morpheus' puzzles may be understood as referring to both the gaslight or the schizophrenic understanding of Mental Simulation at the individual level of resolution, Agent Smith's puzzle may refer only to the schizophrenic understanding. Let's consider each in turn.

Neo's puzzle, recalling §4.1's comments regarding normativity, points to the idea that the agency determining norms may be doing so for the sake of implementing control. On the one hand, there is cardinal norming. On the other hand, there is ordinal norming. These correspond with "scaling" in the psychological sciences. The first refers to counting reality, and the second refers to the social/political implementation of norms. The first is supposed to provide insights like: Humans breathe oxygen. The second is supposed to provide insights regarding issues like the segregation of restrooms.

Interestingly, then, when Neo asks his "Analyst" to help him clarify a cardinal norm, The Architect – as agent of the Matrix – responds to him as if all cardinal norms are ordinal norms,[36] which is a form of gaslighting (cf. Dorpat, 1996). At the same time, if Neo's doubt is unable resolve the (ultimately soteriological) ambiguity at the heart of the mental type of Simulation, then he will not be able to resolve the ambiguity regarding Morpheus' distinction. This is precisely the difference between the gaslight understanding of Mental Simulation at the individual level and the schizophrenic understanding.

Similarly, Morpheus' *puzzle* (not Morpheus' distinction), points to a similar soteriological ambiguity. Morpheus posed the following question for Neo, "Is reality based in memory nothing but fiction?" For, this too can be

---

[36] Neo, speaking to the Architect asks, "Am I crazy?" To which The Analyst authoritatively responds, "We don't use that word in here."

understood as either a form of gaslighting or a –
considering a *normal* interpretation of the mind –
psychotic. As with Neo's puzzle, the ambiguity is ultimately
soteriological, because if "we" are "in" an individual mental
type of Simulation, then to be psychotic, to be "crazy," to
be schizophrenic may be understood as an indicator or
"unplugging" from the Simulation.

The most extreme interpretation is exemplified by Agent
Smith's identity puzzle. For example, in the context of a
solipsistic understanding of individual Mental Simulation,
it follows that "other minds" are, more or less, agents of the
Simulation. Thus, an attitude of soteriologically-
ambiguous paranoia belongs here, because the individual
can believe itself to be working against a force – the agency
of the Simulation itself – manifesting across different
individuals, that is, "other minds."

From a pan-mental point of view, a Mental Simulation may
be understood in terms of fantasies validated by feelings,
controlling beliefs. In fact, it may be possible to interpret
the Buddhist Five Aggregates Theory in this way.
Suddenly, Mother's calming caresses are blue pills. Yet, at
the same time, if one attempts to resolve the ambiguity of
the Mental by believing they are trapped in a solipsistic
Simulation, then the value of violence is not immediately
clear.

For instance, killing others might remove them from your
Simulation, but it would not remove the Simulation itself.
This is exemplified in *The Matrix: Resurrections* by showing
that the Architect survives being killed by Agent Smith.
However, recalling The Architect's puzzle, Trinity seems to
get gratification from harming The Architect, despite all
parties involved knowing that it is merely a Simulation-
based infliction of violence.

In sum, Dainton's discussion of consciousness from our
Introduction is open to both the gaslighting and the
schizophrenic understandings of Mental Simulation at the
individual level of resolution. Just as it was possible (at the

social level of resolution) to understand consciousness as grounded in sociality, so too it is possible at the individual level to understand simulated consciousness as either selectively or fully solipsistic.

§6.2 When?

The question "When?" regarding Mental Simulation at the individual level of resolution invokes the idea of the Mandela Effect. Namely, the idea that history is somehow being altered. Stated in a different direction, it invokes Morpheus' puzzle and the idea of "false memory." Of course, this also invokes the film *The Mandela Effect* (2019).

Further, as should come as no surprise at this point, the question of "When?" points directly to another problem launched by Descartes along with his *cogito ergo sum* and his problem of other minds. In Meditation III of Descartes' *Meditations on First Philosophy* (1640), there is a problem that referred to nowadays as "The Five Minute" problem. Though not as popular as the Mind/Body problem, this temporal problem refers to Descartes' attempt to deny the truths of mathematics.

Basically, Descartes' method of hyperbolic doubt led him to doubt the veracity of "everything" until he found something that could not be doubted. Of course, when one is doubting, then one cannot doubt that one is doubting. And, since doubt is a kind of cognition, that is, a kind of thinking, then Descartes was able to conclude, "I think; therefore, I am," (in Latin: *cogito ergo sum*). That is how Descartes moved from hyperbolic doubt to the solipsistic certainty that he existed.

Yet, prior to arriving at his cogito ergo sum, Descartes needed to find a way to doubt the truths of mathematics. Descartes' hyperbolic way to provide a reason how the truths of mathematics can also be doubted, gave birth to the "Five Minute" problem. According to Descartes's strategy, when someone is adding 2 + 3 and expecting to arrive at 5, there is a way that the conclusion 2 + 3 = 5 may be false. How is that? If an evil demon (or if you are merely a "brain in a vat") were to wait until you start performing the equation, then after you move past the 2, the evil demon may change the meaning of "2" from "2" to "4." In this way, after you add the "3" to the "2" (which is now really "4"), then the correct answer would no longer be "2 + 3 = 5." Rather, the answer would be "7." Thus, for Descartes, even the truths of mathematics may be doubted.

Notice, two points regarding this problem from Descartes' *Meditations*. First, it is ground in time. It requires the passing of time to be able to be a problem. Second, it sounds precisely like *The Mandela Effect* (2019) and *The Butterfly Effect* (2004). Ultimately, the idea is that the past can be changed, and this applies directly to Mental Simulation at the individual level of resolution. For, if individual Mental Simulation is true, then – like déjà vu in *The Matrix* – the past grounded in the Simulation can be changed. Moreover, this would be true of both a gaslighting and a schizophrenic understanding of Mental Simulation, at the individual level.

Given all of this, how should we conclude regarding the "When?" question? On the one hand, if we take a pan-mental understanding of Mental Simulation, then time may be merely an aspect of the Simulation. If reality refers to the mind-external and there is nothing mind-external (because the simulated reality of the Mental Simulation is understood as pan-mental), then time may simply be a fabrication of the Simulation.

On the other hand, *if* we take a mind-external understanding of Mental Simulation, given that the ontology of that which is mind-external, regarding Mental Simulation, would necessarily be ambiguous, *then* the truth of time would be undecidable. In other words, even if there is something outside the Mental Simulation, given that it is with the mind that we *understand* anything and everything, then it is not clear that we could ever

183

understand its relation to time. It is important to keep in mind, here, that we are not talking about mind-external reality as actuality. If that were the case, then we would be talking about the actual type of Simulation, not the mental type. Hence, the answer to the "When?" question, regarding Mental Simulation at the individual level of resolution depends on whether one takes a mind-external or pan-mental approach to understanding Mental Simulation.

§6.3 Constraints

Perhaps the best way to state the constraints regarding Mental Simulation at the individual level of resolution in terms of the phenomenology's *Welt*-matrix. Recall, the *Um-Welt, Mit-Welt, Selbst-Welt,* and *Eigen-Welt* refer to that which physically surrounds us, our participation in the "with-world" or relations to other beings, our relation to ourself (specifically as a body), and our relation to spirituality or be-ing itself, respectively.

On the one hand, Mental Simulation may be articulated in terms of the *Selbst-Welt* as the ground of the other *Welt*s in the *Welt*-matrix. On the other hand, each of the other *Welt*s in the *Welt*-matrix, and even the *Welt* aspect of the *Selbstwelt*, are to be understood as simulated, that is, as manifestations of the Simulation. Thus, it is possible to consider the distinction between the gaslight and the schizophrenic understandings of Mental Simulation.

In answering the question of "When?" above the constraints regarding understanding the truth of history and time were already discussed. In regard to the gaslight understanding of Mental Simulation, we are constrained from being able to soteriologically differentiate regarding Morpheus' distinction. Are there cardinal norms – suggestive of a mind-external understanding of Mental Simulation? Or, are there only ordinal norms – suggestive of a pan-mental understanding of Mental Simulation? Ultimately, solipsism is at the root of the constraints regarding Mental Simulation.

§6.4 Transcendence

Transcendence regarding the mental type of Simulation at the individual level of resolution is interesting in that the constraints may be seen as benefits. Thus, the gaslight understanding of Mental Simulation is quite straightforward. When someone begins to question the norms of "reality," and, in truth, that reality is a simulated reality, then it is a benefit to the individual to question reality and their own relation to what is "normal." In terms of the interpretation of reality pushed by the Matrix, Neo's abnormality is a step toward his transcending the Simulation.

The schizophrenic understanding of Mental Simulation is slightly more complicated. There is a difference between the "philosophical" and the "psychological" understanding of the term "schizophrenia." Whereas the psychological – more properly, the "psychiatric" – understanding of the term schizophrenia unambiguously refers to mental illness and brain dysfunction, the philosophical understanding of the term has a wider meaning.

Perhaps the best exemplar of the philosophical understanding of schizophrenia is to be found in Deleuze and Guattari's characterization in their two-volume *Capitalism & Schizophrenia* (1972 & 1980). Though Deleuze and Guattari were not working within the context of Simulation theory, a direct analogy may be made. If Capitalism – more specifically the kind of mentality and world-view that manifests through the development of economic and technological forces – is understood as a Simulation, then the abnormality of schizophrenia may be understood as resistance to such a world-view.

Just as foreign territory may be occupied, the concept of "territorialization" refers to the manner in which an interpretation can become the dominant way something is understood. Territorialization may be understood as functioning ubiquitously throughout the *Welt*-matrix. In other words, one can gain an idea from within the *Selbst-*

welt and apply it to understand the *Um-welt*. In such a case, the idea from the *Selbst-welt* may be said to have territorialized the *Um-welt*. Hence, to think of beings in the *Um-welt* as commodities (including one's body and time) may betray that one's worldview been territorialized by Capitalism.

Thus, the schizophrenic understanding of Mental Simulation may be understood – *by the Individual* – as resistance to being territorialized by the Simulation. As indicated by some of the social backlash to the first *Matrix* film and as depicted at the end of *The Glitch in the Matrix* documentary, this peculiarity regarding Mental Simulation at the Individual level of resolution makes Morpheus' distinction unresolvable.

The schizophrenic point of view regarding Capitalistic territorialization is problematic because it is as if neither side of the debate can gain traction to persuade the other side. On the one side, we have an individual who sees the schizophrenic understanding of reality as incoherent or symptomatic of illness. On the other side, we have an individual who sees disorganized thinking – non-capitalistically organized thinking – as a benefit (perhaps even a "blessing"). Or, perhaps, even to attempt to articulate a coherent place for such an individual in Simulation theory is to misunderstand such an individual.

This renders Morpheus' distinction unresolvable insofar as both sides of the distinction (who is in the Simulation and who is not?) could see the other as being in the Simulation. The person with the Capitalistic worldview sees the schizophrenic as incoherent and lost in some kind of non-reality. In contrast, the schizophrenic – if they have a coherent understanding of the person with the Capitalist worldview or not – would, according to Deleuze and Guattari, see the coherency of the Capitalist point of view stemming from the commodification of reality which has led them into living in a Simulation.

Conclusion

Dr. Pittman

The goal of this work was to analyze the evidence for Simulation Theory and construct a framework for exploring the artifacts of such a Simulation. The artifacts are necessary if Simulation were real. Let me say upfront that I am not more-or-less convinced we reside within a Simulation after reaching the conclusion of this work. I am, however, convinced that (a) a simulated reality is computationally feasible and (b) some types and resolutions are more possible than others. At the same time, I think Simulation Theory is not pure science fiction. There exists a tangible, palpable logic to the possibility we inhabit some form of computer-generated Simulation. I maintain our work here has demonstrated such.

Simulation Theory is reaching an inflection point in culture. The documentary, *A Glitch in the Matrix* is a worldwide phenomenon. Popular movie and fiction have picked up the scent as well and produced some of the most lauded works in modern times such as *The Matrix* trilogy. While both examples have a deep debt to Philip K. Dick pondering what evidence might determine if our reality was somehow fabricated, one reality amongst a host of concurrent and laterally aligned realities.

Like PKD and the protagonists in *The Matrix*, our journey in this chapter began with the question, a*re we living in a machine-generated Simulation?* Why is the question of whether we are agents within a Simulation important to discuss though? It is legitimate to also ask why knowing that one lives in a Simulation would be important.

The implications of Simulation are far-reaching and deep enough that Man has pondered these questions in one form or another for millennia. Indeed, the idea that reality may not be *real* encapsulates problems of what gives rise to human consciousness, problems of free will, and even problems of Mankind's place in the universe.

Fair enough.

Of course, there have been attempts to definitively answer the question of whether we exist in some form of Simulation. This work differs in that we are not trying to answer *if* we inhabit a Simulation. Rather, this work brings into focus a logic for understanding under what conditions Simulation Theory may be true.

To properly situate *truth* in this sense, one must come to terms with the body of source material at the foundation of this work. There are two means to do so: chronologically or combinatorically. We favor the combinatoric approach because synthesis of concepts drives the approach as opposed to unidirectional, linear flow of time.

Speaking of synthesis, there are two foundational film-based overviews. On the fictional side, we have *The Matrix* trilogy. The filmmakers embedded a healthy summary of relevant philosophy throughout the three films while situating the narrative in an overtly cyberpunk context. On the nonfiction side, the documentary *A Glitch in the Matrix* is has grown in popularity since its release. The documentary is broad in its treatment of Simulation Theory, supplying an increasingly bleak view of non-simulated reality.

All of the films owe a great deal to the text-based foundational material. Chiefly, Philip K. Dick's fiction and non-fiction established a phenomenology for Simulation Theory. As a matter of fact, PKD cemented many of the artifacts associated with the function and form of simulated reality. From *when* (time) to *how* (machine | programmer), it is impossible to not trace backwards to work such as *Do Androids Dream of Electric Sheep, A Scanner Darkly,* and of course the *Metz Lecture.*

Conclusion

With that said, one of the strongest attempts to situate the truth of Simulation Theory has only come recently with the Bostrom Simulation argument paper. In fact, Bostrom has produced a series of papers collectively outlining his probabilistic model. However, even more telling is the enormity of follow-up work derived from Bostrom in recent years. The dialogue is, without a doubt, ongoing.

Naturally, any consideration of Simulation Theory must contend with the positions held by luminaries such as Plato, Descartes, Baudrillard, and Deleuze. Computation and technology drive any potential Simulation. Figuring out whether reality is real is the province of the general and fundamental questioning long forming the backbone of philosophy. Unfortunately, throughout the related work there is not a usable map one can use to discover the important attributes of Simulation Theory. To that end, I hope this book serves as a roadmap for your adventure through artifacts of the Simulation.

The artifacts are a continuous degree of what, how, and when Simulation exists relative to the observer residing in an Actual, Social, or Individual level of Simulation Resolution. The more Actual the Simulation, the more *technologically* oriented the artifacts, and to the right more *psychologically* extreme artifacts.

For instance, in the Actual Simulation case, the computational logic is something like there is a physical Machine in base reality that generates what is a copy of the base reality universe as a simulated equivalent. Comparatively, the logic for Virtual Simulation replaced the copy of base reality with a virtual reality as the Simulation. Finally, Mental Simulation went a fair bit further and exposed mental states or phenomenological experience as the operational logic.

If you are like me, you have wondered what the distinction is between *a copy of base reality* and a *virtual reality*. The answer, which I believe this work has brought forth, is as follows. A copy is just that, a bit for bit, element for element copy. We would experience the copy firsthand. A virtual reality would be the same in terms of bits and elements. However, we would experience it through *something.* In the context of current, 21ˢᵗ century technology this *something* might be a virtual reality headset such as Oculus. In the context of this work, the *something* is a virtualization substrate or hypervisor.

Simulation types are broad categories though. We can use the type categories like scaffolding to probe deeper into the secrets of living in Simulation. To add to this, we arranged the three levels of Simulation resolution as interconnecting structures across the three types. The Universal resolution applies to the *universe* or the set of all things. In contrast, the Social resolution is a microcosm of the Universal just as society is a bounded subcategory and social groups within a society more so. In either case, we define the essence of the Simulation as the interaction between the Social and the Simulation elements. Then, the Individual further compartmentalizes Simulation to level of the person.

I think the above is a fair summary of the logic Frank and I have uncovered while exploring Simulation Theory. Well, that is a summary from my computational theorist perspective. I recognize throughout this book I have provided half of the picture at best. I think my half establishes the computational foundation for a potential Simulation. However, I certainly find Frank's philosophical perspective not only insightful but also a critical form of competition for the overarching idea. I know I find a new idea or unique way to think about one of the artifacts every time I read through his sections.

Speaking of innovative ideas, my part of this work is missing some information and ideas. Such are missing because I either could not find a way to make them fit into our matrix of Simulation artifacts (e.g., quantum computing) or the idea didn't occur to me until now. Regardless, I want to use the remaining time and space available to me to impart those ideas and leave us with some direction as to how to proceed from here.

With all that said, I think we should not take this work literally as it relates to technology.

First, as I worked through the main sections of the book, I observed something *meta* to the types and resolutions. Specifically, the shifting of Simulation artifacts as we changed levels of resolution within a specific Simulation type produces a meta progression. On one hand, I think it is obvious that we started with artifacts highly tangible and fixed and ended with artifacts fluid and transient. Yet, on the other hand, I have observed subtextual connections between types and resolution.

For example, it seems to me the Individual level of resolution is a small step away from the Universal resolution of the next Simulation type. In contrast, the divide between the Simulation types at the same resolution- say, Actual-Social compared to Virtual-Social- was not so small or subtle. This leaves me wondering if the progression of Actual to Virtual to Individual represents a blueprint for how a base reality civilization might progressively construct a Simulation.

In other words, start simple and build up to complexity.

Here, I think Frank's points regarding *modes of production* seem to indicate Simulation is inevitable. Is this unreasonable to suggest? Well, there are no computational reasons to think Simulation is not inevitable. While philosophy is not my principal field of study, I am tangentially aware of some main ideas related to computational theory and so forth. For instance, Ellul's[37] concept of *technique* as it applies to social technological progress feels compatible.

---

[37] Ellul, Jacques. *The Technological Society.*

It also has occurred to me the Actual and Mental types of Simulation are extreme poles with the Virtual type as a middle ground. Often, I think of the spectrum of types and sets of resolutions as representative of a normal distribution (i.e., bell curve). This makes me wonder if the predominant fixation with video games and virtual reality in the modern source material lends credence to the viability of the Virtual Simulation type. Of course, it is possible my background and profession bias me.

It is not bias to assert the Universal set contains *everything* computational even non *universal* constructs. Discrete mathematics establishes this as fact. While I alluded to such Set Theory constructs through the book, I avoided one obvious point which I'm wondering if you picked up on. There is a nonzero possibility of the Machine combining all three Simulation resolutions to construct the overall Simulation experience. The Machine would nest the Individual within the Social and the Social nested within the Universal. Such an architecture is the epitome of the computational recursion I mentioned in my Preface.

But what about the Simulation types? I think it is also possible for Actual, Virtual, and Mental to not just coexist but to cooperate in producing the overarching Simulation. The Machine affects recursion again to nest the Mental-Individual within a Virtual-Social which nests in the Actual-Universal. I think the proper guidance for thinking about this comes from the subtextual connections between types and resolution I mentioned earlier in this conclusion.

We should wonder then about what kind of Machine might be capable of rendering such Simulation. Well, one related idea I opted to not deal with in the main chapters is that of a base reality Machine so powerful it could run all three types of Simulation, each with all three levels of resolution, as a persistent and omnipresent construct. It seems to me this kind of architecture describes the *metaverse*[38] in

---

[38] The social environment known as *Second Life* is a primitive incarnation of this idea. More recent relative to this work is Facebook's rebranding as Meta

general terms. Admittedly, not all the computational technology necessary to construct a metaverse exists as of this writing but we are not far off.

I also want to note multiple Simulations may exist concurrently. However, we only see insider our Simulation. We don't know whether Simulations power the other individuals, societies, or universes. At the Virtual-Social level of resolution for example this could refer, for example, to different potential life Simulations in which individuals participate.

It is as if Social ordering is itself the imposition of some ordering that is not a real ordering, it is a Virtual ordering. Standing in line when there is no line to stand in is to simulate the reality of a line. It is to act as if there is an Actual line when there is no actual line. Computationally there is little or no differentiation between such lines. The Machine generates a real line just as well as a Virtual line.

On that note, I struggle with the idea of a civilization capable of optimizing a Simulation indistinguishable from reality and the idea of constructing a Machine not 100% reliable and robust. Those ideas seem at odds. This also might be difference between Actual and Virtual or Actual and Mental. There can be a glitch in the sense that the Simulation *misses* reality. If we imagine a time sequence in the base layer of reality, then we might experience glitches as taking no time at all. It could be the case that the time it takes for the Programmer to create something new and splice it into the Simulation occurs disjoint from the Simulation timeline. The effect would be like pausing a video game, inserting a change to a part of the game not actively rendered, and unpausing.

I'll end with this thought: it does seem like some form of Simulation is inevitable. I think there is value in attempting to reveal whether such Simulation is a future possible or if

---

with the intent of providing a fully augmented and virtual reality for its userbase.

we inhabit a Simulation already. Hopefully, the computational blueprints laid out in this work help us discover the intersection of those ideas. While I made some allusions to input technique, I refrained from extended discourse on the matter. I don't know if the differences between a stream and a packaged batch process matter except in some technical performance analyses.

Conclusion

Dr. Scalambrino

The ontological goal, so to speak, of this book was not to identify the *one answer* to Simulation Theory's central question ("Do we live in a Simulation?"), as if Simulation Theory were itself nothing more than a closed, Yes or No, question.

Rather, the hope was to provide an overview of Simulation Theory. This is valuable, for example, because readers interested in the Simulation Hypothesis, formulating Simulation Arguments or questions regarding Simulation Theory can use such an overview to understand the bigger picture of the questions intriguing them.

I believe we have accomplished that goal. That is to say, all together these chapters function as a reference book for Simulation Theory.

What we have found is that Simulation Theory divides into different types of Simulation. In essence the different types of Simulation are the different ways to understand Simulation in general. Thus, the first question readers interested in Simulation Theory should ask is: What is meant by Simulation?

It turns out that the term "Simulation" can be understood, generally, in different ways. After significant research and copious examination, we identified three (3) ways Simulation can be understood. They are: Actual Simulation, Virtual Simulation, and Mental Simulation.

In turn, each of these general ways of understanding Simulation may be understood, specifically. In other words, each general category of Simulation divides into the species of Universal, Social, and Individual. We refer to these species as "levels of resolution" regarding whichever general understanding of Simulation is being examined, whichever understanding of Simulation is being discussed.

Personally, I consider this to be a highly valuable contribution to the scholarship regarding Simulation Theory. Now that we are in the Conclusion section of the book, my goal for this section is to report which general and specific types of Simulation seem most probable, viable, and tenable.

Thus, I have divided my portion of the Conclusion section into the following seven (7) sections.

(1) Critique and Clarification: On Simulation Theory as Unfalsifiable
(2) Aristotle's 4 Causes & Simulation Theory
(3) Living "Off-the-Grid": Urban Life as a Virtual Social Simulation, We Live in a [Simulated] Society
(4) Technologically-Mediated Self Relation: "The Double" as Virtual Individual Simulation
(5) The *Welt*-Matrix as Chakral Projection and Virtual Universal Simulation
(6) Ethics as Hypervisor: From Mental To Actual Individual Simulation
(7) Death Rattle of the Last Pre-Singularity Paradigm? From Cyborg Anthropology and Trans-Humanism to Post-Humanism

These sections divide in the following way. The first two sections regard Simulation Theory as a theory. The next four (4) sections – Sections 3 thru 6 – refer to possible ways in which Simulation Theory may be true. That is to say, these four (4) sections refer to ways in which Simulation Hypotheses may be understood as true.

Finally, the last section articulates Simulation Theory in regard to another set of standard perennial topics in philosophy of technology. Those topics usually go by the names: "Cyborg Anthropology," "Trans-Humanism," and "Post-Humanism." This juxtaposition, and articulation, is important because these topics provide a wider context for understanding Simulation Theory. That is to say, Simulation Theory may be understood as a revelation functioning within a larger revelation, namely, the context of these topics.

Conclusion

Conclusion 1, Critique and Clarification: On Simulation Theory as Unfalsifiable

The issue of a theory or hypothesis being "unfalsifiable," hearkens back to philosophers of science such as Karl Popper (1902-1994), Paul Feyerabend (1924-1994), and Thomas Kuhn (1922-1996). The basic idea is that if a theory is unfalsifiable, then it is not "scientific." Further, if a theory isn't scientific, then it is a matter of faith. It is more like religion than science, since scientific theories are theories that can be falsified.

Back in 1994, to claim a theory was unfalsifiable was to condemn it to death, as far as academicians were concerned. Yet, in 2022, the *Zeitgeist*, so to speak, is quite different. Basically, the fact that Simulation Theory is unfalsifiable, the fact that evidence cannot be identified that would determine it false, doesn't seem doesn't seem to curb people's interest in it.

This points, in my opinion, to an observation which came to me immediately upon looking into Simulation Theory. What I immediately observed was that Simulation Theory, especially Actual Simulation, seems to be a technological articulation of Early Modern "mechanical" ontology and philosophy of religion. The same philosophical questions asked by philosophers such as René Descartes (1596-1650), Benedict Spinoza (1632-1677), Gottfried Wilhelm Leibniz (1646-1716), and William Paley (1743-1805).

In particular, William Paley's "Watchmaker Argument" continually came to mind. Paley's argument basically holds that the universe evidences sufficient design to suggest a designer. Of course, Simulation Theory holds that the universe (or our experience of it) exhibits sufficient design to suggest that it may be a Simulation. There may be a programmer, and so on.

Now, two last points regarding this conclusion. First, if you go by its "trending" capacity, it doesn't seem to be a sufficient critique of Simulation Theory to say that it is unfalsifiable. In other words, perhaps Simulation Theory belongs in the category of spirituality and religion, not the category of scientific theories of reality or existence.

Second, when we inquire how to philosophically understand Paley's Watchmaker Argument, we find that Paley's Argument is a kind of teleological argument. On the one hand, that means that it uses function and complexity to evidence purpose. On the other hand, teleology should point to Aristotle's "Final Cause" of his famous "4 Causes." So, the next conclusion regarding Simulation Theory as a theory involves its articulation in regard to all of Aristotle's 4 Causes.

Conclusion 2, Aristotle's 4 Causes & Simulation Theory

Recall that Aristotle's 4 Causes (sometimes referred to as "Be-Causes") are the Material, the Efficient, the Formal, and the Final.[39] In the language of Simulation Theory, the Material Cause refers to base reality. The Efficient Cause refers to the Programmer of the Simulation. The Formal Cause refers to the Hypervisor, insofar as it determines the type of Simulation. Finally, the Final Cause refers to the purpose, or lack thereof, of the Simulation.

Similarly, the How and When questions we use to explicate each level of resolution regarding each type of Simulation, refer to the ontology of the Simulation. Like Aristotle's 4 Causes. In contrast, then, to the ontological aspects of Simulation Theory, the soteriological aspects refer to questions such as Can and Should. In this book, we discussed these aspects in terms of Constraints and Transcendence.

A clarification may be in order regarding the Efficient Cause. In the Actual Simulation chapter of this book, I note that none of us are responsible for generating the Simulation. However, in both Virtual and Mental we may

---

[39] Aristotle's 4 Causes originally come from Plato. They can be found in Plato's *Timaeus*. I wrote at length about this in my *Introduction to Ethics* textbook, published by Kendall Hunt in 2016.

be responsible for generating the Simulation, for example, in terms of Capitalism or some forms of technologically-mediated "hive mind," belief, or mental illness. So, the Efficient Cause may be understood in multiple ways that coincide with how Simulation is understood.

Simulation Theory as a theory, then, involves all the components we would expect of a philosophical theory. Further, if Simulation Theory is to be situated in the category of spirituality and religion, then it is also possible to classify each of the general types of Simulation Theory. For example, Actual Simulation would refer to a type of Cosmological or Theological Theory. Virtual Simulation would refer to a Cosmological, a Theological or a Psychological Theory, and Mental Simulation would refer to a type of Psychological or Theological Theory. Of course, referring to a theory as a type of Psychological Theory means it could also be referred to as a Social Theory.

Conclusion 3, Living "Off-the-Grid": Ad-based Life as Virtual Social Simulation, We Live in a [Simulated] Society

Of the types of Simulation and ways to understand the meaning of Simulation in Simulation Theory, the Virtual type seems to be the most probable, plausible, and tenable type. One of the easiest ways to see this is in terms of the perennial position in philosophy of technology. That is to say, philosophers of technology have long held that technologically mediating our relation to life and one another has decreased, not increased quality of life.

One of the most interesting articulations of this critique, in my opinion, comes from the many public declarations – even before cell phones existed – that technology was going to reduce the work week, not increase it. For more discussion of this see: *Social Epistemology & Technological Mediation*. The idea, of course, is that technology has increased the amount we work; people are now "addicted" to using devices; and, social media is routinely involved in the destruction of relationships and marriages.

In terms of Simulation Theory, we can look into the extent to which the events comprising a person's life and a person's lifestyle depend upon technology. To the extent, then, that a person's life or lifestyle depends upon technology, it may be possible to identify that life or lifestyle as participation in a Virtual Simulation.

This idea has found linguistic expression in comments like, "That's a first-world problem." That phrase is supposed to indicate how some non-essential aspect of life has become central to one's concerns. When one's concerns are preoccupied with non-essential aspects of life, it suggests that one's life is situated in such a way that one *can* place one's concerns on non-essential aspects of life.

The best example of this, in my opinion, is a concern for gaining "likes" and "followers" on social media. Elsewhere I have characterized such desires in terms of what Epicurus (c.341-270 BCE) called non-natural and unnecessary desires. Epicurus also taught that such "empty and vain" desires know no limit. They amount to creating a monster that can't be fed.

This will be relevant for the next conclusion as well. However, the point to make here is that it is possible to have an entire kind of life – or lifestyle – that is detached from "natural" life. In such instances, the unnatural life would be a kind of Simulation. This is not entirely unlike philosophical debates regarding nihilism. For, some people will suggest that there is no natural existence or that natural existence would be an Actual Simulation. I don't find those arguments credible. However, the urban v. "off the grid" lifestyle question is particularly illuminating for Simulation Theory.

When we consider how popular "2-day shipping" and online-shopping culture has become, it is possible to envision many different lifestyles concerned with non-essential and non-natural aspects of existence. The extent to which these aspects have a form to them – think of how ads are able to sell a kind of lifestyle –, then participation in such lifestyles may be participation in a kind of Simulation.

Thus, as discussed throughout the chapter on Virtual Simulation, various social forms of life may be understood as Virtual Simulations. Whether we seek to blame Capitalism, some nefarious spiritual force, or human folly, clearly there are people existing today who are so alienated from their own natural existence that their life may be understood as participation in a Virtual Simulation.

Conclusion 4, Technologically-Mediated Self Relation: "The Double" as Virtual Individual Simulation

This conclusion is a more psychologically-oriented version of the previous conclusion. It also conjures up Baudrillard's notion of "the double."[40] Thus, the idea in this conclusion is that one's self-understanding can become so dependent upon technology that thinking of one's self in that way may be participation in a Simulation.

Here is an interesting example. Currently on Amazon, there is a book in a genre that comes up first whenever you search for that genre. Further, the author has no formal education in the topic about which that author has written. And, yet, that book has more five-star reviews than the acknowledged Classics and progenitors of that genre. Now, when you look more closely, you realize that this individual is just very good at utilizing Ads and leveraging for reviews (not at writing or philosophizing).

That example is interesting because, you have a person who has strategically spent money to occupy a certain position on social media. Does this person look at their massive (paid-for) following and count it as evidence of their amazingness? Notice, of course, this is a kind of Virtual Individual Simulation. Further, it calls to mind Baudrillard's criticisms of Post-Modernism.

---

[40] I highly recommend reading Baudrillard's *The Perfect Crime* published by Verso (not the censored free pdf version floating around the internet).

There has been at least one philosophy professor whose strategic affiliations and funding put them in a scene in which the President of the United States handed them an award for writing a philosophy book. I wonder if such philosophy professors consider themselves "great philosophers" because they receive an award from POTUS.

On the one hand, what immediately emerges to the foreground is the meaninglessness of such technologically-mediated awards. On the other hand, such award winners could respond that for the people who buy into the Simulated reality in which such authors deserve such awards it is Virtually real. That's Post-Modernism. Arguing for the reality of an obvious illusion on Democratic grounds.

Ultimately, the point of this conclusion was to indicate that a Virtual Individual Simulation is quite plausible, probable, and tenable. Interestingly, it is not much of a stretch at all to think that many individuals understand their existence and the quality of their existence in terms of a technologically-mediated (Virtual) reality.

And, connecting back up with the previous conclusion and the above chapter on Virtual Simulation, many of these "Influencers" would point to monetization and passive income as the indicator that their Virtual Simulation is more actual than Virtual. Thus, we see the link between Capitalism and Simulations.

It could be argued that Socio-Economic Status (SES) conditions a spectrum of possible self-identities and social experiences available to humans. If that is the case, then, SES functions as a kind of hypervisor for Virtual Simulations. If there is some kind of "off-the-grid" or significantly less technologically-mediated existence, then perhaps that would be a non-Simulated human life.[41]

---

[41] Cf. Scalambrino, Frank. "How Technology Influences Relations to Self and Others: Changing Conceptions of Humans and Humanity." *Social Epistemology Review and Reply Collective* 6, no. 3 (2017): 30-37.

Conclusion 5, The *Welt*-Matrix as Chakral Projection and Virtual Universal Simulation

One of my favorite ideas taken from phenomenology is the idea that "the world" is a kind of thematization of phenomenal experience. There are many factors that could be said to influence thematization. However, the immediate criticism that arises when regarding this topic should be addressed at the start. The criticism against the idea that the world depends on a thematization performed by an existing individual is that the identity of the world cannot be simply open-ended.

Thus, to address that criticism, it is not that thematization is open-ended; rather, it is that there is a range of possible thematizations. Once we recognize this, then we are able to understand that some thematizations are closer to the natural flow of real (base reality) phenomena and others revolve around a technologically-mediated logic.

Or, put differently, other thematizations are further away from base reality. In fact, we need not even embrace Realism here. We can simply say that even if no thematization could possibly "get reality right with a Capital 'T' truth," it is still possible that some thematizations are closer to such a characterization than others.

The thematizations that are "further" from the ineffable truth of base reality are so many Virtual Simulations when compared with base reality. The question then becomes: How could such thematizations be Universal?

The thematizations – including the ones that participate in *forms* of Simulation – could vary, not in terms of the identity of entities but, rather, in terms of natural potencies. In other words, *it could be the case that humans are rooted in base reality by potentialities and that the actualization of those potentialities may be in accordance with forms that are congruent with base reality and with forms that are less congruent with base reality.*

In this way, the spectrums of possible thematizations would be Universal because the natural potencies would be Universal. One way, then, to envision how such potencies may be Universal is to recognize the way the *Welt*-matrix relates to natural potencies, for example, those associated with the Chakras.

Rather than provide a long drawn-out and deeply researched characterization here, I think it is sufficient to note that the *Um-Welt* as the "lowest" in the *Welt*-matrix would coincide with the lowest Chakras and the *Eigen-Welt* as the "highest" would coincide with the highest Chakras.

Hence, if we envision how these two trajectories may be correlated, we can envision the spectrum of possible thematizations available for each *Welt* as correlated with the Chakras. Just as there could be a harmony associated with the ability to thematize in terms of congruency with base reality, so too there could be harmonious thematization along each trajectory – harmony amongst the Chakras, harmony amongst the thematizations of the *Welts*.

It seems to me, then, that this is a probable and tenable characterization of Virtual Universal Simulation. Whatever number of individuals happens to be thematizing in terms of an incongruency with base reality, that number of individuals is potentially thematizing in terms of the same form of Simulation. In such an instance, those individuals would be participating in a Virtual Universal Simulation.

Conclusion 6, Ethics as Hypervisor: From Mental to Actual Individual Simulation

Conclusions 2, 3, 4, and 5, just above, may help us understand this conclusion. The idea here is that insofar as the hypervisor may be understood as generating a Simulation in terms of its form, then ethics may be understood as a hypervisor. That is to say, how an individual thematizes the world, according to the *Welt*-matrix, may correlate with that individual's ethics.

Interestingly, then, this understanding of the hypervisor involves all the nuances initially noted regarding hypervisors at the beginning and throughout this book. That is to say, the ontological constitution of the hypervisor varies in regard to the type of Simulation in question.

As we will see, the characterization being worked out here could be used to render either an Actual or a Mental Simulation probable. In order to understand how this is the case, recall what above was referred to as "the mereology of Mental Simulation at the Individual level of resolution."

In order to understand this mereology, there are three different ideas to track. First, reality may be understood as pan-mental (all mind). Second, within such an understanding, the individual may be distinguished from the pan-mental by merely being, or having access to, a part of the All-Mind, not the whole. Lastly, of course, base reality may be mind-external despite phenomenal reality's being pan-mental.

In the first case, the *form* of one's *ethos*, how one relates to experiential reality, may be responsible for manifesting both the phenomenal content of the world and how one thematizes the world. In the second case, the individual's Mental Simulation may be understood as diverging from a congruency with a pan-mental base reality (Mental Universal Simulation) by only being, or having access to, a part of the pan-mental, rather than the whole.

Lastly, if we apply the logic of the pan-mental to an Actual that is mind-external, then we can understand how ethics could function as a hypervisor in an Actual Simulation also. Hence, we can envision how ethics may be understood as a hypervisor in regard to Mental and Actual Simulation at the Individual level of resolution.

Thus, the idea of projection is important here. Just as the world may be a Chakral projection governing thematization, ethics may govern the projection.

Conclusion 7, Death Rattle of the Last Pre-Singularity Paradigm? From Cyborg Anthropology and Trans-Humanism to Post-Humanism

The mathematization of Nature (perhaps it is better to say the pan-mathematization of Nature), it seems to me, is antithetical to Existentialism. It is antithetical to Transcendental Philosophy. This is the primary difference between Descartes and Kant. Kant provides us access to a transcendental dimension that cannot be mathematized – at least not by us. Moreover, supposing an AI could mathematize it, the extra-dimensionality to which Transcendental Philosophy gives us access is unknowable to us. Thus, it would always be a matter of trust. Trusting the information we give to the AI and trusting the information it gives us back – without ever being able to verify/falsify it.

Despite this important and essential distinction, it seems to me the majority of humans on this planet are operating with a Cartesian worldview. The Cartesian worldview is no doubt powerful. It gave us Cartesian coordinates and all that we can now do with an X/Y graph. However, it is simply not the case that being able to provide a mathematical characterization of the reality to which we have experiential access will provide us certainty to the questions of existence.[42]

Now, how is all this relevant for Simulation Theory? The idea that the majority of people on this planet are operating with a Cartesian worldview suggests that they believe there is some kind of mathematical certainty regarding existence, the problem is simply being able to perform the calculation. In this way, it is as if they belief the movie *Limitless* could *actually* be true. As noted in Chapter 1, above, such belief in the pan-mathematization of existence denies the role of chance/destiny involved in (re)incarnation.

---

[42] Just because I can arrange my options in an algorithm does not mean the algorithm removes the operations of destiny in regard to the selection of options nor does it remove freedom of choice.

Conclusion

Despite this critique of the pan-mathematization of reality, there are many Social influences which seem to make it Virtually true. What I mean is that the presence of the internet and social media makes it appear that, for example, every question can be answered by Googling it. Dr. Pittman and I come from a special generation, in a sense, because we have been able to experience both realities – the reality of not having the internet and social media and the reality of having the internet and social media.

What the presence of the internet and social media implies is that all the answers are potentially available to us. That implication, in turn, depends on a pan-mathematical (Cartesian) worldview. Now, *even if that worldview is not true, the belief in it has consequences.*

For example, the idea that there is one best answer to solve existential problems or with which to navigate existential issues is highly problematic. One, it is true that the shortest distance between two points may be a straight line; however, the terrain that straight line traverses may not be wise to traverse. Two, the implication that there is one best answer for existence suggests that there is a *form* of life that is best.

Once everyone starts living as if that form is the ideal life, then those individuals will be living, for all intents and purposes, in a Virtual Simulation. I'm not suggesting a non-sophisticated mathematization of reality. Perhaps the *Um-Welt* may have a less sophisticated mathematization than the *Selbst-Welt*; however, we are taking into consideration here the mathematics of contingency showcased, for example, at the end of *Limitless* – namely a complicated web of "if, then" statements informed by the digital processing of the environment (*Um-Welt*).

Hence, I acknowledge that within the context of the Cartesian worldview, each individual may have a different equation identifying the path they should take from their here-and-now to the "right answer," that is, to their ideal existence. Yet, the point I am making is that the "right answer" regarding the *Selbst-Welt* (and especially the *Eigen-Welt*) is occluded from mathematization. Even if there is a perfect way to design the lawn, the best existential path to traverse with our choices cannot be revealed to us (at least not in this incarnation).[43]

Lastly, it seems we are back at the soteriological point that we have been making throughout this book. That is, being in a Simulation seems to equate to a kind of existential inauthenticity. If it is possible to be in a Simulation, then it is not the most primordial existence for us; rather, it is something that we – using the term from Existentialism – *fall* into. I am reminded of Novalis' observation: "Building worlds is not enough for the mind that reaches more deeply."[44]

Put directly, though the question of Simulation Theory is ultimately ontological, the answer to that question is soteriologically grounded. The old saying of the ancient Greek philosophers resounds: Ethics is first philosophy.

Thus, when the paradigm with which humans view the world is a Cartesian worldview, then they act as if there is a mathematically correct form (functioning as an ideal). And, to live in accordance with such a worldview is to participate in a Simulation. This is how cyborgs are made. This, in my opinion, is philosophically a fundamental premise of Cyborg Anthropology.

Further, it is the basis for affirming the Trans-Humanism movement. If turning myself into a robot makes me more efficient at performing x, y, and z, then why wouldn't I want to algorithmatize myself? Though "winning" in that world may, in fact and in terms of that world, be winning, do I

---

[43] In fact, technically speaking, not even time travel would solve this problem, unless only one person could time travel, but, even then, that person's choices would be constrained by the period(s) of time in which they chose to eventually live. Thus, in time travel, the existentiality of life gets pushed to a meta-level.

[44] Novalis. (1997). "Miscellaneous Observations." *Philosophical Writings*. M.M. Stoljar (Translator). §90.

really want to use my life force to win in that world? Whatever the answer to that question is, the existential opportunity cost is inescapable. Algorithmatizing myself for one Simulation may be at the cost of algorithmatizing myself for a different Simulation. This is where the idea of the Singularity comes in.

To conclude, even if there were one *singularly* best algorithm with which to algorithmatize myself, doing so would amount to plugging into the Matrix, if there is an Actual base existential reality that is not a Simulation to which the Singularity's algorithm applies. It is precisely the move into Post-Humanism. Not Post-Humanism in the ambiguous good way (see my discussion of Humanism from *What is Existentialism, Vol. II*). Rather, it is the kind of Post existence into which one falls, despite attempting to land in a Trans existence.

Bibliography & Further Reading

Althusser, Louis. (2014). *On the Reproduction of Capitalism: Ideology and Ideological State Apparatuses*. G.M. Goshgarian (Trans.). London: Verso.

Aristotle. (1984). *On the Soul*. J.A Smith (Trans.). In J. Barnes (Ed.). *The Complete Works of Aristotle: The Revised Oxford Translation*. Vol. II. (pp. 641-692). Princeton, N.J.: Princeton University Press.

_____. (1995). *Metaphysics*. W.D Ross (Trans.). In J. Barnes (Ed.). *The Complete Works of Aristotle: The Revised Oxford Translation*. Vol. II. (pp. 1552-1728). Princeton, N.J.: Princeton University Press.

_____. (2009). *Nicomachean Ethics*. R. Crisp (Trans.). Cambridge: Cambridge University Press.

Barthes, Roland. (1978). "Death of the Author." Stephen Heath (Trans.). In *Image, Music, Text*. New York: Hill and Wang, 142-149.

Baudrillard, Jean. (2010). *Agony of Power*. Hodges (Trans.). South Pasadena, CA: Semiotext€.

_____. (2005). *The Conspiracy of Art*. A. Hodges (Trans.). South Pasadena, CA: Semiotext€.

_____. (2008). *The Perfect Crime*. C. Turner (Trans.). London: Verso.

_____. (2017). *Simulacra and Simulation*. S.F. Glaser (Trans.). Ann Arbor, MI: University of Michigan Press.

Benjamin, Walter. (2006). "The Work of Art in the Age of Its Technological Reproducibility." Harry Zohn (Trans.). In *Walter Benjamin: Selected Writings, Volume 4, 1938–1940,* edited by Howard Eiland and Michael W Jennings. 251-283. Cambridge, MA: Belknap Press of Harvard University Press.

Bostrom, Nick. (2003). Are You Living In a Computer Simulation? *Philosophical Quarterly*, Vol. 53, No. 211, pp. 243-255.

Chalmers, David J. (2022). *Reality+: Virtual Worlds and the Problems of Philosophy*. London: W.W. Norton.

Chun, Wendy Hui Kyong. (2006). *Control and Freedom: Power and Paranoia in the Age of Fiber Optics*. Cambridge, Mass.: The MIT Press.

Dainton, Barry Francis. (2002). Innocence Lost: Simulation Scenarios: Prospects and Consequences. (pp. 1-24). Unpublished Paper. https://www.simulation-argument.com/Dainton.pdf. Last Accessed: 01/02/2022.

Deleuze, Gilles. (1992). "Postscript on the Societies of Control." *October*, Vol. 59. (Winter), pp. 3-7.

Deleuze, Gilles, and Félix Guattari. (2003). *Anti-Oedipus: Capitalism and Schizophrenia, Vol. I*. London: Continuum.

_____. (1988). *A Thousand Plateaus: Capitalism and Schizophrenia, Vol. II*. London: Athlone Press.

Dick, Philip. K. (1995). *The Shifting Realities of Philip K. Dick: Selected Literary and Philosophical Writings*. New York: Vintage.

Dorpat, Theodore L. (1996). *Gaslighting, the Double Whammy, Interrogation, and Other Methods of Covert Control in Psychotherapy and Psychoanalysis*. New York: Jason Aronson.

Dorrestijn, Steven. (2012). Theories and figures of technical mediation. In *Design and Anthropology*. J. Donovan and W. Gunn (Eds). 219-230. Burlington, VT: Ashgate.

Ellul, Jacques. (2000). "Ideas of technology: The technological order." *New Perspectives Quarterly* 17(3): 21-30.

_____. (1964). *The technological society*. J. Wilkinson (Trans.). New York, NY: Vintage Books.

Fish, Jefferson M. (2015). "A University Is Not Walmart."
    Psychology Today (Feb. 03).
    https://www.psychologytoday.com/blog/looking-in-the-
    cultural-mirror/201502/university-is-not-walmart.
    Last accessed 05-16-2022.

Floridi, L. (2014). *The Fourth Revolution: How the Infosphere is
    Reshaping Human Reality.* Oxford: Oxford University
    Press.

Foucault, Michel. (2010). *The Government of Self and Others:
    Lectures at the Collège de France, 1982-1983.*
    Basingstoke: Palgrave Macmillan.

_____. (2004). *Security, Territory, Population.* G. Burchell
    (Trans.). New York: Palgrave Macmillan.

_____. (2003). *"Society Must Be Defended": Lectures at the
    Collège de France, 1975-76.* New York: Picador.

Furness, Dyllan. (2019). "Are we living in a simulation? This
    MIT scientist says it's more likely than not". *Digital
    Trends [Online]*, April 9.
    https://www.digitaltrends.com/cool-tech/we-spoke-to-
    an-mit-computer-scientists-about-the-simulation-
    hypothesis/. Last accessed: 05-16-2022.

Gramsci, Antonio. (1971). *Selections from the Prison Notebooks.*
    Translated and edited by Q. Horare and G.N. Smith.
    London: Lawrence & Wishart.

Grasnick, Armin. (2022). *Basics of Virtual Reality: From the
    Discovery of Perspective to VR Glasses.* London:
    Springer.

Green, Ronald M. (2007). *Babies by Design: The Ethics of
    Genetic Choice.* New Haven: Yale University Press.

Gutiérrez-Maldonado, José., Marta Ferrer-Garcia, Alejandra
    Caqueo-Urizar, Elena Moreno. (2010). "Body Image in
    Eating Disorders: The Influence of Exposure to Virtual-
    Reality Environments." *Cyberpsychology, Behavior, and
    Social Networking* 13: 521-531.

Hanson, F. Allan. (2004). "From classification to indexing: How Automation Transforms the Way We Think." *Social Epistemology: A journal of Knowledge, Culture and Policy* 18(4): 334-356.

Hardt, Michael, and Antonio Negri. (2001). *Empire.* Cambridge MA: Harvard University Press.

Heidegger, Martin. (1962). *Being and Time.* J. Macquarrie and E. Robinson (Trans.). New York: Harper & Row.

_____. (1984). *Early Greek Thinking.* D.F. Krell and F. A. Capuzzi (Trans.). New York: Harper & Row.

_____. (2008). The Question Concerning Technology. In D.F. Krell (Ed.) *Basic Writings.* (pp. 307-343). London: Harper & Row Perennials.

Johnston, John. (2008). *The Allure of Machinic Life: Cybernetics, Artificial Life, and the New AI.* London: The MIT Press.

Jünger, Ernst. (1963/1983). "Technology as the Mobilization of the World through the *Gestalt* of the Worker." Translated by J. M. Vincent, revised by R.J. Kundell. In *Philosophy and Technology: Readings in the Philosophical Problems of Technology*, edited by C. Mitchum and R. Mackey. 269-89. New York: The Free Press.

Kant, Immanuel. (2006). *Critique of the Power of Judgment.* P. Guyer and E. Matthews (Trans.). Cambridge: University of Cambridge Press.

_____. (1998). *Critique of Pure Reason.* P. Guyer and A.W. Wood (Trans.). Cambridge: University of Cambridge Press.

_____. (1960). *Religion Within the Limits of Reason Alone.* T. M. Greene and H. H. Hudson (Trans.). New York: Harper & Row.

Kehe, Jason. (2022). "Of Course We're Living in a Simulation." *Wired [Online]*, Mar. 9. https://www.wired.com/story/living-in-a-simulation/. Last accessed: 05-16-2022.

Bibliography & Further Reading

Khan, Fouad. (2021). "Confirmed! We Live in a Simulation". *Scientific American [Online]*, April. https://www.scientificamerican.com/article/confirmed-we-live-in-a-simulation/. Last accessed 05-16-2022.

Kisiel, Theodore. (2014). "Heidegger and Our Twenty-First Century Experience of Ge-Stell." In *The Multidimensionality of Hermeneutic Phenomenology*, edited by B. Babich and D. Ginev. 137-152. New York: Springer.

Knöpfel, Thomas., and Edward Boyden, editors. (2012). *Optogenetics: Tools for Controlling and Monitoring Neuronal Activity*. New York, NY: Elsevier.

Kurzweil, Ray. (2005). *The singularity is near: When humans transcend biology*. New York: Penguin Books.

Ling, Thomas. (2021). What causes déjà vu? The quirky neuroscience behind the memory. *Science Focus [BBC Online Magazine]*. https://www.sciencefocus.com/the-human-body/deja-vu/. Last accessed: 05-16-2022.

List, Christian and Pettit, Philip. (2010/2011). *Group Agency: The Possibility, Design, and Status of Corporate Agents*. Oxford University Press.

Lohr, Steve. (2015). *Data-sim: The Revolution Transforming Decision Making, Consumer Behavior, and Almost Everything Else*. New York: Harper Collins.

Loscerbo, John. (1981). *Being and Technology: A Study in the Philosophy of Martin Heidegger*. The Hague: Martinus Nijhoff.

Lyotard, Jean-François. (1979/1984). *The Postmodern Condition: A Report on Knowledge*. G. Bennington and B. Massumi (Trans.). Minneapolis: University of Minnesota Press.

Mahoney, M.J. (1977). "Publication prejudices: An experimental study of confirmatory bias in the peer review system." *Cognitive Therapy and Research* 1: 161-175.

Marcel, Gabriel. (1962). The Sacred in the Technological Age. *Theology Today* 19: 27-38.

Marcuse, H. (1991). *One-dimensional man: Studies in the ideology of advanced industrial society*. Boston: Beacon Press.

Marin, Louis. (2002). *On Representation*. Catherine Porter (Trans.). Stanford, CA: Stanford University Press.

_____. (1984). *Utopics: The Semiological Play of Textual Spaces*. Robert A Vollrath (Trans.). New York: Humanity Books.

Marx, Karl. (1992). *Capital: A Critique of Political Economy, Vol. I*. B. Fowkes (Trans.) London: Penguin.

Mayer-Schönberger, V., and K. Cukier. (2013). *Big Data: The Revolution that Will Transform How We Live, Work and Think*. London: John Murray.

McDermott, Jim. (2022). "We're not living in a simulation—and we need to stop acting like we are." *American Gazette [Online]*. February 03. https://www.americamagazine.org/politics-society/2022/02/03/. Last accessed 05-16-2022.

Mounk, Yascha. (2018). "What an Audacious Hoax Reveals About Academia." *The Atlantic* Oct. 5.

Mullins, Eustace. (2009). *The Secrets of the Federal Reserve*. New York: Bridger House Publishers.

Nietzsche, Friedrich. (1974). *The Gay Science [aka The Joyful Quest]*. W. Kaufmann. (Trans.). New York: Vintage.

_____. (1980). *On the Advantage and Disadvantage of History for Life*. P. Preuss (Trans.). Indianapolis: Hackett.

_____. (1968a). *Twilight of the Idols/ The Anti-Christ*. R.J. Hollingdale (Trans.). Middlesex, England: Penguin.

_____. (1968b). *The Will to Power*. W. Kaufmann and R.J. Hollingdale (Trans.). New York: Vintage Books.

Novalis. (1997). *Philosophical Writings*. Albany, NY: SUNY.

Offe, Claus. (2012). "Whose good is the common good?" *Philosophy and social criticism* 38: 665-684.

Ong, Walter J. (1982). *Orality and literacy: The technologizing of the word*. London: Methuen.

Peters, Douglas P. and Stephen J. Ceci. (1980). "A Manuscript Masquerade: How well does the review process work?" *The Sciences* 20(7): 16-19.

Plato. (1997). *Timaeus*. D.J. Zeyl (Trans). *Plato Complete Works*. John M. Cooper (Ed.). Indianapolis, IN: Hackett Publishing.

Radder, Hans. (2010). "The commodification of academic research." In *The commodification of academic research: science and the modern university*, edited by H. Radder. 1-23. Pittsburgh: University of Pittsburgh Press.

Robinson, Bruce. (2015). "With a Different Marx: Value and the Contradictions of Web 2.0 Capitalism." *The Information Society* 31: 44-51.

Rosen, Larry D., K. Whaling, S. Rab, L. Mark Carrier, and Nancy A. Cheever. (2013). "Is Facebook creating 'iDisorders'? The Link Between Clinical Symptoms of Psychiatric Disorders and Technology Use, Attitudes and Anxiety." *Computers in Human Behavior* 29(3): 1243-1254.

Scalambrino, Frank. (2021). *What Is Existentialism, Vol. I*. Castalia, OH: Magister Ludi Press.

_____. (2017). "How Technology Influences Relations to Self and Others: Changing Conceptions of Humans and Humanity." *Social Epistemology Review and Reply Collective* 6, no. 3 (2017): 30-37.

_____. (2015). *Social Epistemology & Technology*. Edited Volume. London: Rowman & Littlefield International.

_____. (2015). The Temporality of Damnation. In R. Arp and B. McCraw, (Eds.). *The Concept of Hell*. New York: Palgrave.

_____. (2014). From a Statement of Its Vision Toward Thinking into the Desire of a Corporate Daimon, *Social Epistemology Review and Reply Collective* 3(10): 34-39.

_____. (2014). "Social Media and the Cybernetic Mediation of Interpersonal Relations." In *Philosophy of Technology: A Reader*, edited by F. Scalambrino. 123-133. San Diego, CA: Cognella.

Short, Tim. (2015). *Simulation Theory: A Psychological and Philosophical Consideration.* London: Psychology Press.

Szasz, Thomas. (2003). *Pharmacracy: Medicine and Politics in America.* New York: Syracuse University Press.

_____. (2010). *The Myth of Mental Illness.* New York: Harper Perennial.

Vaihinger, Hans. (1949). *The Philosophy of As If.* C.K. Ogden (Trans.). London: Routledge & Kegan Paul.

Ward, Adrian F. (2013). "Supernormal: How the Internet is Changing our Memories and our Minds." *Psychological Inquiry* 24: 341-348.

Wiener, Norbert. (1965). *Cybernetics, Or, the Control and Communication in the Animal and the Machine.* London: MIT Press.

Wittgenstein, Ludwig. (1972). *On Certainty.* D. Paul and G.E.M. Anscombe (Trans.). New York, NY: Harper & Row.

_____. (1922). *Tractatus Logico-Philosophicus.* London: Kegan Paul, §5.6.

Index

ARTIFACTS OF
THE SIMULATION:
A Reference Book
for Simulation Theory

~~~~~~~~~~~~~~~~

Written by

Jason M. Pittman

&

Frank Scalambrino

Winston-Salem, NC: Pirino Books
MMXXII

Printed in Great Britain
by Amazon

37222718R00131